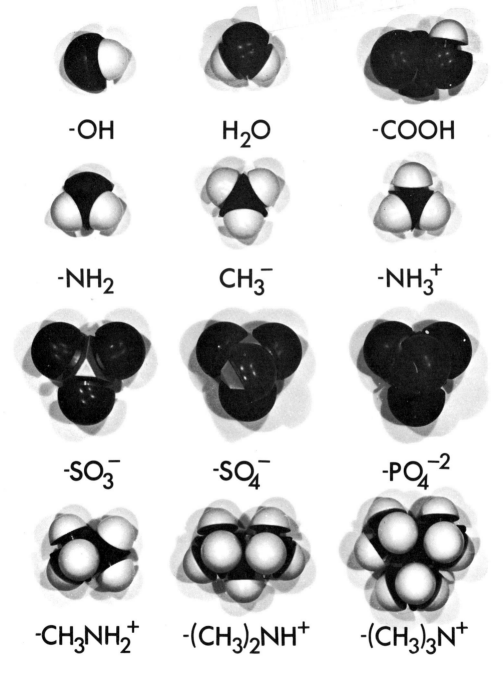

-OH H_2O -COOH

$-NH_2$ CH_3^- $-NH_3^+$

$-SO_3^-$ $-SO_4^-$ $-PO_4^{-2}$

$-CH_3NH_2^+$ $-(CH_3)_2NH^+$ $-(CH_3)_3N^+$

Water and
Solute-Water Interactions

J. LEE KAVANAU

University of California, Los Angeles

Water and Solute-Water Interactions

1964

HOLDEN-DAY, INC.

San Francisco, London, Amsterdam

PREFACE

To lay the groundwork for the development of theories on the structure and functions of biological membranes for a recent monograph (Kavanau, 1964), the author treated extensively many pertinent aspects of molecular and interfacial chemistry. Included in this program was a comprehensive review and discussion of the current theories and status of research in the fields of water structure and water-solute interactions. Because of the general interest of this material for researchers and students in many areas of the physical and chemical sciences, it is reprinted here without modification. References to chapters refer to the complete work, *Structure and Function in Biological Membranes*, Volumes I and II, to be published later this year.

In general, all major viewpoints are presented, with comprehensive literature citations. In many areas several theories leading to more or less similar or to quite dissimilar conclusions are able to coexist, because definitive experimental evidence is not at hand. I have not sought to smooth over the complexities of the problems nor the tangle of the many existing discrepancies. Although this would give a more specious and easily digestible view to the casual reader, it would give a quite misleading one to the researcher and serious student. It is instructive and sobering to be aware of the wide latitude of disagreement that exists over the interpretation of even the most elementary intermolecular phenomena, particularly in aqueous media.

I am greatly indebted to Drs. R. Aranow, G. W. Brady, R. E. Connick, G. Eisenman, E. Forslind, H. S. Frank, O. Jardetzky, B. Kamb, L. B. Magnusson, S. Meiboom, G. Némethy, C. T. O'Konski, L. Pauling, and H. A. Scheraga for many helpful suggestions, comments, corrections, or personal communications concerning parts or all of the manuscript. I am pleased to acknowledge the generous research-grants support of The National Science Foundation and The National Institute of Mental Health, U. S. Public Health Service.

J. Lee Kavanau

CONTENTS

To James L. Van Vliet

THE STRUCTURE OF ICE

Ordinary ice, ice I (density, 0.924 g/ml; filling factor 0.34), has a highly open centrosymmetric structure (fig. 1) similar to that of the hexagonal form of silica (SiO_2) known as "tridymite" (see Barnes, 1929; Bernal and Fowler, 1933; Pauling, 1935, 1960; Owston, 1958). The oxygen atoms lie in layers, with each layer consisting of a network of open, puckered, hexagonal rings. The oxygen atoms alternately are raised and lowered, each layer being a mirror image of adjacent layers (the structure being in the ABAB···· sequence). Water molecules retain their individuality but participate in four hydrogen bonds. Each oxygen atom is surrounded tetrahedrally at a distance of 2.76A by the four other oxygen atoms to which it is hydrogen-bonded. The hydrogen atoms, however, are distributed asymmetrically, lying on lines connecting adjacent hydrogen-bonded oxygen atoms but closer to one oxygen atom than to the other. Each oxygen atom has two hydrogen atoms near it (the two hydrogen atoms of the molecule) at an estimated distance of about 0.96 to 1.02A (0.958A in the vapor), linked to it by strong bonds, and two farther away (the hydrogen atoms of two neighboring molecules) at an estimated distance of about 1.74 to 1.80A. The unit cell contains four water molecules. This scheme of colinear hydrogen-atom arrangement and hexagonal structure has been confirmed beyond reasonable doubt by neutron diffraction experiments on D_2O ice I (Peterson and Levy, 1957).

Each interstitial region of ice I is bounded by six water molecules at a distance of 2.945A from its center. At the same time each water molecule is the nearest-neighbor of three cavities. The dimensions of the interstitial regions between the coordinated tetrahedra (fig. 1) are greater than the dimensions of the water molecule; Samoilov (1946, 1957b) and Forslind (1952, 1953) propose that each of these regions can accommodate a free, non-associated molecule without greatly disturbing the structural order.

The water molecules in ice I undergo thermal vibrations around their equilibrium positions, the intermolecular movements being both dilational and deformational (Forslind, 1953). The root-mean-square amplitude of vibration of the water molecule (assuming that it vibrates as a single unit) is approximately 0.44A at −10°C (see Owston, 1958). All proton configurations compatible with the conditions mentioned above have nearly the same lattice energy and therefore occur with equal probability, giving a proton-disordered structure (statistically, two "half-hydrogen atoms" lying along each O·····O bond) which does not become ordered on cooling (Pauling, 1935; Wollan, Davidson, and Shull, 1949; Forslind, 1952; Peterson and Levy, 1957). Studies of ice I in an alternating electric field near the melting point show that the proton configurations are highly mobile and vary with time under the influence

1

of thermal fluctuations; the proton configuration "freezes in" at about $-183°C$ (see Bjerrum, 1952; Coulson, 1957).

Apart from the six high-pressure ice polymorphs—ice II and ice III discovered by Tammann (1900) and ices IV, V, VI, and VII discovered by

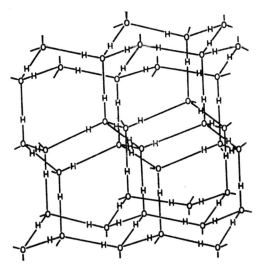

Figure 1. Schematic representation of the crystal structure of ice at low pressure. (After Barnes, 1929.) (Reproduced by courtesy of Drs. G. Némethy and H. A. Scheraga, and the American Institute of Physics from the Journal of Chemical Physics.)

Bridgman (1912, 1935, 1937)—only two other forms of ice are known to exist with certainty: a cubic cristobalite-type structure, ice Ic, having the same zero-point entropy as ice I (König, 1942, 1944; Honjo, Kitamura, Shimaoka, and Mihama, 1956; Lisgarten and Blackman, 1956; Blackman and Lisgarten, 1957, 1958; Shallcross and Carpenter, 1957; Gränicher, 1958), and an ice of uncertain but probably amorphous structure, "vitreous ice" (Burton and Oliver, 1935; Vegard and Hillesund, 1942).

Vitreous ice can be produced only by condensing pure water vapor on a surface maintained below $-160°C$. It undergoes a partial and irreversible change to ice Ic at higher temperatures (see Honjo, Kitamura, Shimaoka, and Mihama, 1956; Blackman and Lisgarten, 1958; Dowell and Rinfret, 1960). Although some investigators have assumed that vitreous ice is a glassy form, König (1942) and Vegard and Hillesund (1942) suggest that it is composed of small crystallites. According to Dowell and Rinfret (1960), domains may exist in which there is a tendency toward the same layer structure present in ices Ic and I, but with random distribution of the molecules within the layers.

Ice Ic (density, 0.923 g/ml; filling factor, 0.34) also can be formed at low rates of deposition, low pressures, and temperatures of about -140 to $-80°C$ (see Shallcross and Carpenter, 1957; Lonsdale, 1958; Fernández-Morán, 1960)

or by heating ices II, III, or V (Bertie, Calvert, and Whalley, 1963). Above −130°C, ice Ic (and vitreous ice) transforms to ice I at a rate that depends markedly on the thermal history of the sample (König, 1942, 1944; Dowell and Rinfret, 1960; Beaumont, Chihara, and Morrison, 1961; Bertie, Calvert and Whalley, 1963). The latter transition probably was observed first by Dewar (1905). Ice Ic can be considered to be built up of puckered layers of oxygen atoms identical to those of ice I but with each successive layer shifted half the diameter of a hexagonal ring, leading to the ABCABC····· stacking sequence typical of the diamond cubic system. Another way of viewing the difference is that the three bonds radiating from each of the two oxygen atoms at the ends of a given O·····O axis are "opposed" (eclipsing) in ice I and "staggered" in ice Ic (as in the eclipsed and staggered conformations of ethane). The unit cell contains eight water molecules (König, 1944); the O·····O distance is 2.75A; the O—H distance is approximately 0.97A; and the protons are disordered as in ice I (Honjo and Shimaoka, 1957). No significant infrared spectroscopic difference can be detected between normal and deuterated ice I, ice Ic, and vitreous ice (Hornig, White, and Reding, 1958).

A systematic study of the crystal structures of the high-pressure forms of ice has been undertaken in Kamb's laboratory (Kamb and Datta, 1960; Kamb, 1964; see also Lippincott, Weir, and van Valkenburg, 1960; Bertie, Calvert, and Whalley, 1963), the ultimate results of which may advance our understanding of the structure of liquid water and the energetics of the hydrogen bond. The high-pressure polymorphs (ices II to VII) are stable at pressures exceeding about 2,000 atmospheres; they can, however, be studied by X-ray diffraction at atmospheric pressure because they can be maintained metastably at sufficiently low temperatures (Tammann, 1900; McFarlan, 1936).

Ice II (density, 1.17 g/ml) occupies the lowest-temperature portion of the pressure-temperature field investigated by Bridgman and forms only by transformations from other solid phases. It has twelve water molecules in a rhombohedral unit cell with each oxygen atom bound to the four nearest-neighbors at a distance of about 2.80A and having a next-nearest neighbor at 3.24A (Kamb, 1964). It is most remarkable that the protons in ice II appear to be ordered, whereas all other ice polymorphs appear to be proton-disordered (Kamb, 1964).

In ice II a relatively small but significant perturbation of a basic structure (or pseudostructure) in space group R3̄c is believed to be caused by long-range ordering of the protons. The pseudostructure contains ice-I-like units built of puckered six-membered rings of water molecules. Apparently there is freedom for the bond angles to deviate markedly from the "ideal" tetrahedral values, so that ice-I-like units can be linked together in a more compact way than in ice I. The hydrogen-bond strain energy, although greater than in ice I, is small enough to be offset by the extra van der Waals-London energy, so that the energy of ice II is only 10 cal/mole greater than that of ice I.

Kamb assumes that the distortion from the pseudostructure occurs in such a way as to bring the O·····O·····O angles presented to the H—O—H groups (donor angles) closer to the angle for which the hydrogen-bond energy is a maximum.*

Bridgman's (1912) measurements indicate that the entropy of ice II is 0.77 cal/mole-degree less than that of ice I over the range −75 to −34°C. Kamb's findings suggest (assuming that the difference in lattice vibrational entropy between ice I and ice II is small) that this measured value is a direct reflection of the entropy of the proton disorder in ice I. One of the potentially most significant findings to emerge from Kamb's analysis is that the strain-energy contribution from the hydrogen-bond acceptor depends primarily upon a deviation from the "accepting plane" that bisects the H—O—H angle of the molecule, rather than upon a deviation from the tetrahedral-bond orientation relative to the accepting water molecule.

Ice III (density, 1.14 g/ml; filling factor 0.44) is dimensionally cubic but symmetrically tetragonal (Kamb and Datta, 1960; Bertie, Calvert, and Whalley, 1963). The arrangement of the oxygen atoms can be interpreted in terms of hydrogen-bonding (Kamb and Datta, 1960), but appreciable deviations from the ideal tetrahedral configuration of the water molecules are present, as in ice II (Kamb, 1963). There are twelve water molecules in the unit cell and each oxygen atom is surrounded by four others at distances of 2.78 to 2.81A. The arrangement of the oxygen atoms is very similar to that of the silicon atoms in keatite, a high-pressure polymorph of SiO_2 discovered by Keat (1954). The latter relationship thus extends the already known structural relationships between the silica and ice polymorphs[†] (ice I-tridymite and ice Ic-cristobalite).

X-ray powder patterns for ice V have been published by Bertie, Calvert, and Whalley (1963), but the unit cell is not known. Powder data also have been obtained for ice VI but have not been analyzed yet (Kamb and Datta, 1960).

To account for the high dielectric constant of ice I (up to about 100) at low and intermediate frequencies (say at frequencies between 100 and 10,000 cycles / sec at −10 to −2°C), it is necessary to assume that the orientation of the water molecules is changing constantly. Debye (1929) explained the high dielectric constant by the presence of electric dipoles, which frequently turn from one equilibrium position to another under the influence of thermal agitation. Dorsey (1940) calculated the rate of dipole turns per molecule to

* In most hydrates the O·····O·····O angles presented to the water molecules are prevented from adjusting to the angle favored by the water molecules by other steric requirements; thus, the donor O—H bonds deviate by as much as 15 degrees from the O·····O bond. The absence of an ordered arrangement of energetically well-favored angles for H—O—H occupancy may be responsible for the failure of ice I to achieve proton-ordering at low temperatures (Kamb, 1964).

† The favorable energetic relationships involving the proton-ordering peculiar to ice II probably are responsible for the fact that ice II has no analogue among the known polymorphs of SiO_2 (Kamb, 1964).

4

be 8.3×10^5 / sec at 0°C. From the temperature coefficients of dielectric properties, the activation energy for dipole-turning has been calculated to be 13,200 cal / mole (Auty and Cole, 1952).

The mechanism by which the water molecules in ice I become reoriented in an electric field has not been established unequivocally. In an ideal lattice, displacements by proton shifts from one bond to another, no matter how devised, either have improbable energy requirements or lead to no net polarization (see Auty and Cole, 1952). Latimer (1949) suggested that the high dielectric constant of ice might be due to the "atomic polarization" of the proton in the bond. He suggested that dipole reorientation in ice depended upon the jumping of the protons over the potential barrier in the hydrogen bond, rather than upon rotation of the water molecules. However, this method leads to equally serious difficulties with energy requirements and appears to have other shortcomings. Thus, for example, if excitation to the first vibrational level of the stretching mode of an O—H bond is a rate-limiting process (this might logically be a prerequisite to proton-tunneling through and along O—H bonds), the activation energy for D_2O should be only about $\sqrt{2}$ / 2 of the value for H_2O (see O'Konski, 1963). Since this is not the case, the dielectric polarization process in ice probably does not involve proton-tunneling. Schellman (1951; see also Schellman and Kautzmann, 1951) proposed that there were missing hydrogen bonds between a few of the oxygen atoms as a result of lattice defects or vacancies and that molecular reorientations through the lattice were made possible by propagation of the missing bonds.

The subsequent model of Bjerrum (1952) accounts for the electrical properties of ice I by postulating the existence of thermal lattice defects of two kinds—ionic and orientational. Ionic lattice defects are formed by the migration of protons from one oxygen atom to another, giving rise to an equal number of H_3O^+ and HO^- ions. Orientational (or valence) lattice defects are formed by the rotation of water molecules through 120° about an O—H·····O axis or, perhaps, by a rotational jump of a proton within the same molecule (Gränicher, 1958). Such a rotation generates one vacant O·····O separation (L-defect) and one doubly occupied O—H·····H—O separation (D-defect) (fig. 2a,b). A subsequent or coupled rotation of the adjacent water molecule into the vacant site separates the D- and L-defects, which migrate in this manner through the crystal.

Two molecules between which there is an L-defect can rotate easily into new positions. Every time one of the molecules rotates, the defect is moved (structural diffusion) and the dipole moment is rotated through 90°. L-defects accordingly might be said to promote dipole-turning (Bjerrum, 1952). The concentration of thermal Bjerrum defects decreases exponentially with decreasing temperature and is calculated to be one per 10^8 hydrogen bonds at 0°C. The concept that the hydrogen configurations are changed only by the diffusion of Bjerrum defects leads to a consistent theory of the electrical, mechanical, and thermal properties of ice.

5

Dunitz (1963) suggested, however, that the existence of colinear D-defects was unlikely. Thus, the Bjerrum model would imply a separation of only 0.78A between the two hydrogen atoms in the doubly-occupied bond (D-defect). This separation distance would correspond to an enormous (and

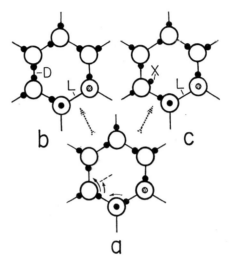

Figure 2. Schematic representation of the formation of a DL (a → b) and an XL (a → c) pair of orientational defects. (After Dunitz, 1963.)

unrealistic) increase in the mutual repulsion energy (estimated at 60,000 cal / mole) over that for the shortest hydrogen-hydrogen distances known (assuming any reasonable form of the potential energy curve in this region). Moreover, the D-defect must correspond to an energy maximum with respect to the rotation of one or both of the participating water molecules, so that although it might conceivably correspond to a transition state, Dunitz argued that it could not correspond to a stable arrangement of water molecules (see also Cohan, Cotti, Iribarne, and Weissmann, 1962).

To overcome these shortcomings of the Bjerrum model, Dunitz proposed that a water molecule rotates only 60° about an O—H·····O axis, bringing its second hydrogen atom into a position midway between an O—H·····O and an empty O·····O (L-defect) direction. A subsequent or coupled rotation of the adjacent water molecule through 120° brings its hydrogen atoms into the empty O·····O region (fig. 2a,c). The combination of these two rotations was felt to produce an energetically more reasonable and stable arrangement than a D-defect, one in which the "extra" hydrogen atom is situated symmetrically between two neighboring O·····H—O bonds, being about 1.5A from each of its two nearest-neighbor hydrogen atoms on other molecules. This latter situation, referred to as an "X-defect," is separated from the L-defect, which cannot diffuse back spontaneously.

Once the Dunitz-defect pair has been formed and separated, both kinds of defects can diffuse through the crystal by "jumps" that involve the rotation of water molecules. The X-defects jump by a coupled rotation of two adjacent water molecules through 60°; the L-defects jump by the rotation of one molecule through 120°. A consideration of the activation energies for the diffusion of these defects indicated that the activation energy for the X-defect was three to five times as great as that for the L-defect. Accordingly, Dunitz suggested that the alternating current conductivity of ice arises almost exclusively from molecular rotations associated with the diffusion of the L-defects, the X-defects being present in equal number but being relatively inactive insofar as electrical properties are concerned.

However, Dunitz did not take into account the possibility that relaxational lattice deformations could lower the repulsion and strain energies associated with D-defects. Such relaxation of the lattice might be expected because of the relatively weak bonding in the neighboring $H\cdots\cdots O$ bonds (Eisenberg and Coulson, 1963). When the major relaxational changes in bond lengths and bond angles in the neighborhood of a D-defect are taken into account, the total repulsive and strain energy is reduced from about 60,000 cal / mole of the D-defects to only about 5,190 cal / mole. The latter figure includes the repulsive interaction energy of the two hydrogen atoms, the compressional energy of the two O—H bonds, and the bending and compressional energies of the six nearest H—O—$H\cdots\cdots O$ bonds (Eisenberg and Coulson, 1963). The energy would be even lower if the six nearest-neighbor oxygen atoms were allowed to relax. It is clear from the analysis of Eisenberg and Coulson that the existence of D-defects cannot be ruled out yet. These workers are preparing a detailed comparison of the total energies of formation of both D- and X-defects.

On the other hand, Bergqvist and Forslind (1962) have revived the view that the reorientations of the over-all molecular dipoles, which are responsible for the high dielectric constant of water and ice, take place almost exclusively by way of simultaneous shifts of the proton positions along the hydrogen bonds without the occurrence of free molecular rotation. The individual shifts are proposed to occur as a sort of chain reaction without the disruption of hydrogen bonds. It is suggested that all orientational processes which depend upon lattice molecules and are associated with the dielectric properties, conductivity, flow, etc., of water or ice depend upon such molecular reorientations (Forslind, 1963). The reduction of the dielectric constant of water by ionic solutes is visualized (Bergqvist and Forslind, 1962) as the result of increased lattice distortion and coupling to solute molecules. It is proposed that these effects reduce the probability of unrestricted simultaneous proton displacements because of the increased number of barriers against the rehybridizations which are necessary for proton exchanges between hydrogen-bonded water molecules. As a result, the dielectric constant becomes reduced with increasing solute concentration.

THE STRUCTURE OF LIQUID WATER

The distinctive structural features of liquid water generally have been ascribed to its partial retention of the tetrahedrally directed hydrogen-bonding involved in the crystalline structure of ice* (see references below)—i.e., as a broken-down form of the ice lattice—but with the length of the $O \cdots H \cdots O$ bond increased. Not only are the orientations of the water molecules far from random, but the molecules oscillate torsionally with rather small amplitudes instead of rotating freely. However, free rotation about the axis in the plane of the three nuclei bisecting the H—O—H angle becomes important rather suddenly at about 40°C (see Robinson and Stokes, 1959).

This view of water structure is supported strongly by the results of X-ray scattering experiments and of studies of the infrared and Raman absorption spectra, which indicate that a considerable degree of short-range order and the low coordination characteristic of the tetrahedrally-bonded structure persist in the liquid. Thus, X-ray scattering studies indicate that the average number of nearest-neighbors is 4.4 to 4.6 (probably fluctuating between 4 and 6) and that the average distance between centers is 2.92A. A high concentration of molecules also is found at 4.75 to 4.90A, which is roughly the expected distance (the length of the tetrahedral edge, i.e., $2.92 \times (\frac{8}{3})^{1/2}$) for the next-nearest neighbors if the molecules tend to have a tetrahedral arrangement as in ice (see Morgan and Warren, 1938; Simons, 1939; Finbak and Viervoll, 1943; Gurney, 1953; Brady and Krause, 1957; Brady, 1958; Brady and Romanow, 1960; Danford and Levy, 1962). A distinct maximum at 1.1A is attributed to the closest O—H distance in the water molecule (Danford and Levy, 1962).

Water can be regarded as a particular type of associated liquid in which the association penetrates through the whole volume of the liquid, forming a three-dimensional network, several different configurations of which can coexist simultaneously (see Chadwell, 1927; Bernal and Fowler, 1933; Mikhailov and Syrnikov, 1960). Each of the coexisting configurations corresponds to a characteristic free energy, to characteristic dielectric properties, to a characteristic molecular volume, etc. A change in temperature leads to a change in the relative numbers of molecules associated in each configuration, these shifts accounting for the anomalous properties of water. Most modern theories of water take as a starting point this view that water is a mixture of certain three-dimensional structures.

As useful a guide as these concepts may be to the structure of liquid water, they leave wide latitude in the construction of precise statistical-thermodynamic models.

The "vacant-lattice-point" model. The model of Forslind (1952, 1953) presents the most straightforward departure from the ice I structure and

* Röntgen (1892) was the first to suggest that there are "ice molecules" in water.

achieves considerable success in accounting for the properties of water on the basis of but few assumptions. The liquid phase is regarded as an essentially crystalline system, closely related to a slightly expanded, idealized ice-I lattice (fig. 3). The structure is very open, with the interstitial spaces between the

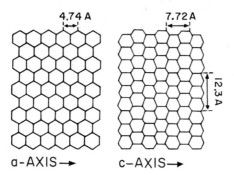

Figure 3. Diagrammatic representation of an ideal water lattice (at 25°C) based upon the ice-I lattice. For a scale molecular model see figure 6. (Reproduced by courtesy of Dr. B. Jacobson.)

groups of molecules in tetrahedral coordination sufficiently large to accommodate free, non-associated molecules without greatly disturbing the structural order. As the temperature of ice is raised, the increasing anharmonicity of the deformational intermolecular vibrations leads to fluctuations in the distribution of the thermal amplitudes, producing localized amplitude peaks that eventually disrupt the weakest bonds. When the thermal amplitudes are sufficient, some of the molecules pass through the faces of the surrounding tetrahedrons and take up interstitial positions.

The resulting lattice defects, each consisting of one vacant lattice point and one interstitial, non-associated molecule (Frenkel defects), increase the anharmonicity of the thermal deformational vibrations of the lattice molecules, greatly enhancing the probabilities of the formation and the propagation of dislocations. Accordingly, the model provides ample opportunities: (1) for molecules to change places; (2) for lone molecules to pass through the faces of the surrounding tetrahedrons to take up interstitial positions (and for their diffusion in lattice interstitial channels); and (3) for lattice defects to diffuse through the lattice, working their way to interfacial boundaries to be annihilated and thus leaving behind lone interstitial molecules (so-called Schottky defects), thereby producing a volume decrease and density increase. The annihilation of the vacant lattice points at the boundaries of the system corresponds to the melting process, the latent heat of fusion of ice being determined by the energy of formation of lone interstitial molecules.

The density increase occurring at the ice-water transition continues until the thermal amplitudes have become sufficiently attenuated by interstitial molecules to prevent the formation of new defects, i.e., until the system has attained thermal equilibrium. The structure of the liquid phase is essentially the same as that of the solid; the chief structural differences are a higher bulk density of the liquid due to the appearance of non-associated interstitial molecules (i.e., new Schottky defects) and an increased number of complete Frenkel defects. In liquid water at 0°C only 9% of the lattice points are computed to be vacant, while the number of interstitial molecules amounts to about 16% of the total number of molecules in the system (Forslind, 1953). The rheological properties of the system depend upon the association of point defects to form dislocations which, under the influence of a shearing stress, will move against a rather small energy barrier to produce the relative displacements constituting the flow process. An excess of interstitial matter will raise the barrier and counteract the flow.

A theory of water very similar to Forslind's was proposed earlier by Samoilov (Samoilov, 1946, 1957b), who evidently was the first to formulate an interstitial model (see also Danford and Levy, 1962). Samoilov also had arrived at the general conclusion that the structure of water (restricted to the short-range order characteristic of liquids) is merely a slightly distorted version of the structure of ice. In his view water molecules which have moved from their equilibrium positions, as a result of the translational movements which become possible on melting, cannot help but pass into neighboring interstitial spaces, which correspond to certain relative potential energy minima. Samoilov proposed that the tetrahedral coordination of ice generally was retained, but that in contrast to ice a definite number of water molecules occupied interstitial sites at any given moment.

The "flickering-cluster" model. The flickering-cluster model of Frank and Wen (1957) and Frank (1958, 1963a) postulates that the formation of hydrogen bonds in liquid water is predominantly a cooperative phenomenon. The existence of a pair of hydrogen-bonded atoms promotes the tendency of each atom to hydrogen-bond to another neighbor, etc. Furthermore, the cooperative element is not limited to linear propagation. Thus, due to a partially covalent character of the hydrogen bond (see Forslind, 1952, 1953; Coulson and Danielsson, 1954; Sokolov, 1956; Coulson, 1957), the remaining lone-pair L-shell electrons of oxygen atoms in a hydrogen-bonded chain of liquid water molecules are more localized, with more nearly tetrahedral sp^3 hybridization, than if the molecules were not members of the chain.* Accordingly, the water molecules are more susceptible to further hydrogen-bonding, which, in turn, imparts additional stability to the existing bond system, giving the process an element of positive feedback.

The net result of the cooperative hydrogen-bonding is that when one bond forms, there is a tendency for several (perhaps many) to form, whereas when

* That redistribution of charge-clouds takes place when a hydrogen bond is formed is shown by several experimental observations (see Frank, 1963a).

one breaks, an entire group tends to break. Accordingly, there are produced short-lived* ice-like, flickering clusters (fig. 4) of varying extent, consisting of highly hydrogen-bonded molecules. The clusters have a high volume-to-surface ratio in which the stabilization per hydrogen-bond for molecules in

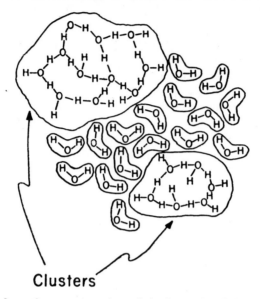

Clusters

Figure 4. Schematic representation of hydrogen-bonded clusters and un-bonded molecules in liquid water according to the flickering-cluster theory of Frank and Wen (1957). The molecules in the interior of the clusters are quadruply bonded, but this is not shown in the diagram. (Reproduced by courtesy of Drs. G. Némethy and H. A. Scheraga, and the American Institute of Physics from the Journal of Chemical Physics.)

the interior is greater than for those at the surface. These clusters are mixed with, and alternate roles with, non-hydrogen-bonded molecules, which form one or two layers between them and constitute the rest of the system, the whole of which is held together by very strong van der Waals-London binding.

No particular assumption about the arrangement of the molecules in the clusters is required beyond the condition that the largest possible number of hydrogen bonds be formed, without an undue distortion arising from departures from bond linearity. In other words the clusters should be compact, with as many quadruply-bonded molecules as possible and with very few extended chains of doubly-bonded molecules. The formation of a cluster occurs

* If the observed dielectric relaxation time in water has as its half-life that of the cluster-forming or cluster-dissolving process, the cluster would have a mean lifetime of 10^{-10} to 10^{-11} seconds (Collie, Hasted, and Ritson, 1948). Since this is 100 to 1,000 times the period of a molecular vibration, it seems long enough to constitute a meaningful existence for the cluster (Frank, 1958, 1963a).

when the stage is set by a local energy fluctuation* which creates a suitably "cold" region; relaxation occurs when the necessary energy of "melting" becomes available, the energy exchanges occurring through collisions at the boundaries of the clusters. The entropy changes associated with the formation and melting of the clusters need not be excessive, for even non-hydrogen-bonded water molecules are by no means rotationally unrestricted, due to the very strong dipole fields of neighboring molecules (Frank and Wen, 1957; Némethy and Scheraga, 1962a).

The difficulty of forming crystallization nuclei spontaneously in supercooled dustfree water is one of the most persuasive arguments that has been advanced against the existence of any small fragments of the ice structure in water (see, for example, Koefoed, 1957). In terms of the flickering-cluster model the failure of neighboring clusters to coalesce rapidly enough to prevent the ready supercooling of water may have the following basis (Frank, 1963a). When an ice-like cluster forms, its faces must display a pattern of partial charge separation on hydrogen atoms and lone-pair electrons which, although systematic, also will possess elements of randomness. The faces of two such clusters will be able to coalesce only if, in addition to the right tetrahedral geometry, they have matching patterns of hydrogen atoms and lone electron-pairs. Since the clusters form separately and in random ways, it would be a rare event for two faces to match exactly—a circumstance which might permit the large amounts of supercooling (to about $-40°C$) actually observed.

In the flickering-cluster model the fulfillment of the condition of a high degree of hydrogen bonding can occur through a large number of structural networks. However, the tridymite-like arrangement in ordinary ice is likely to occur frequently, especially at low temperatures, because it involves a relatively large number of hydrogen bonds for a given cluster size. This model, as formulated in a detailed statistical-thermodynamical analysis by Némethy and Scheraga (1962a, 1962b), leads to the expectation (at 20°C) of an average cluster size of a few molecular diameters, containing an average of 57 molecules. There are about 0.0124 moles of clusters per mole of water. Seventy percent of all molecules would be cluster members with about 23% quadruply-bonded internally and the remaining 47% singly- (23%), doubly- (4%), and triply-bonded (20%) at the cluster boundaries. In terms of hydrogen bonds remaining unbroken relative to ice, the flickering cluster would retain a 46% ice-like character.†

Values for the free energy, enthalpy, and entropy of liquid water calculated by Némethy and Scheraga on the basis of their analysis agree with experimental data to within less than 3%, with the best agreement for the free

---

* The lowering of the potential energy upon cluster formation may be in the neighborhood of 1000 cal/mole bond.

† In the vacant-lattice-point model about 19.3% of the water molecules would be interstitial at 20°C.

energy. The agreement is not as good for the heat capacity which falls off much too quickly with increasing temperature, and the results do not account for the higher-order transitions reported to occur in the neighborhood of 30°C.* Calculated curves for the radial distribution function (the distribution function for the average arrangement of molecules around a given molecule in the liquid) agree well with the X-ray scattering data.

The observed thermal expansion of water is viewed as the resultant of two opposing effects (first suggested by Röntgen, 1892): (1) upon a rise in temperature both the clusters and the unbonded molecules undergo thermal expansion, increasing the molar volume; and (2) the gradual breakdown of the clusters tends to decrease the molar volume. The latter effect occurs because the packing of molecules in the tetrahedrally hydrogen-bonded lattice-work is very poor.† When the hydrogen-bonded structure breaks down, the coordination number increases to about eight, and the void volume is decreased greatly. Effect (2) predominates in the melting of ice, and the theoretical curve reproduces the minimum in molar volume at 4°C. The P-V-T analysis indicates that about 15% of the compressibility of liquid water at 0°C is due to the breakdown of clusters with increasing pressure.

The recent near-infrared studies of Buijs and Choppin (1963) have given results in general agreement with the Némethy-Scheraga analysis and thus tend to support a flickering-cluster model. These investigators have resolved the absorption band of water between 1.1 to 1.3μ into three bands, one at 1.16μ, one at 1.20μ, and one at 1.25μ. They interpret these as representing water molecules with zero, one, and both—OH groups, respectively, hydrogen-bonded to other water molecules. The sensitivity of the method does not permit resolution into subgroups according to proton acceptance, for the effect of proton acceptance on the vibration frequencies is an order of magnitude smaller than the direct effect of the proton being bonded (since the binding electrons of the proton are affected only indirectly). From studies of the temperature dependence of the band intensities, interpreted in terms of a flickering-cluster model, the average size of the clusters and the percent retention of ice-like character could be computed. Agreement between the two calculations is best in the low-temperature range and becomes progressively worse at higher temperatures. From 0 to 72°C the Buijs-Choppin values for the cluster size run from 44 to 145% higher and for retention of ice-like character from 2 to 9% higher than the Némethy-Scheraga values.

Miller (1963) has shown that an excellent empirical correlation exists be-

* It has been suggested that high-order phase transitions occur in water at temperatures in the neighborhood of 15, 30, 45, and 60°C and that the changes in water structure produced at these temperatures have marked effects on protoplasm (see Drost-Hansen, 1956; Lavergne and Drost-Hansen, 1956; Oppenheimer and Drost-Hansen, 1959).

† For tetrahedrally-packed spheres, for example, the void volume amounts to 66% of the total volume, as compared to the well-known value of 25.98% for the closest packing (see Némethy and Scheraga, 1962a).

13

tween the temperature dependence of the viscosity of water, as defined by a free-volume* expression of the form $A \exp (1 / f)$, and the structure of water as given by the Némethy-Scheraga analysis of the flickering-cluster model. The fact that substitution of the volume fraction of unbonded water molecules of the Némethy-Scheraga analysis for the "free-volume" fraction, f, gives an excellent representation of water viscosity appears to demonstrate the effects of internal structural rearrangements which are not reflected directly in changes in total volume. The volume of the unbonded water molecules apparently appears in the above expression as a "free-volume" because only molecules in the unbonded state have the molecular motion required for flow.

The flickering-cluster model offers an explanation for a number of the properties of water, including the characteristic that the energy of activation in liquid water has the same value (4,600 cal / mole), whether calculated for self-diffusion, viscous flow, dielectric relaxation, or the structural relaxation time for excess ultrasonic absorption. This is what one would expect if the principal requirement for any of these processes in water were the breaking down of a rather rigid quasi-crystalline structure, the further steps of accommodation—change of position or orientation of the loosened molecules—requiring little or no energy to activate them (Frank, 1958, 1963a; Singwi and Sjölander, 1960). The flickering-cluster model also makes possible the interpretation of both the structural alteration toward greater ice-likeness which is induced by non-polar solutes (see below) and the fact that this extra ice-likeness seems to be accompanied by a lengthening of the dielectric relaxation time.

The "water-hydrate" model. Claussen (1951) and Pauling and Marsh (1952) showed that water molecules can form structures which, while retaining the bond angles and intermolecular distances characteristic of ice, are "looser" than ice and contain relatively large cavities (empty framework density = 0.8 g / ml). These structures are energetically stable despite their greater "looseness" because, like ice, they are held together by hydrogen bonds. X-ray diffraction studies of von Stackelberg and co-workers (see von Stackelberg, 1949; von Stackelberg and Müller, 1954: von Stackelberg and Jahns, 1954) and Pauling and Marsh (1952) have confirmed that the distances and angles between the water molecules in the hydrates of non-electrolytes differ but little from their corresponding values for ordinary ice.

These hydrates crystallize into two structures (I in space group Pn3m, and II in space group Fd3m; see von Stackelberg and Müller, 1954; Malenkov, 1962) consisting of various polyhedrons, the faces of which are pentagons and hexagons (fig. 5). The gas-hydrate lattice of structure I (cubic unit of structure with an edge of 11.88A) contains almost-spherical cavities with radii of 3.95A and 4.3A. The former is bounded by 20 water molecules at the corners of a

---

* This is not the same as the true free volume, i.e., the *empty space* associated with each molecule, in the Cohen and Turnbull (1959) sense.

nearly regular pentagonal dodecahedron and the latter by 24 water molecules at the corners of a tetrakaidecahedron. The structural types that exist for the gas (and salt) hydrates also may be regarded in terms of the different associations of their polyhedrons, either by sharing faces or by bonding between vertices so as to give rise to host lattices that accommodate the solute molecule without unduly disrupting the hydrogen-bonding scheme of the water framework (Jeffrey, 1962). The solute molecule, in fact, interferes very little with the dynamics of the lattice (van der Waals and Platteeuv, 1958; McKoy and Sinanoglu, 1963). Since it does not collide with the lattice, there can be at most a small barrier to its internal rotation (McKoy and Sinanoglu, 1963).

Compounds of this type, in which certain molecules are constrained in the voids or interstices of a lattice-work formed by other molecules, are called "clathrate compounds" or "clathrates." The hydrates of non-hydrophilic (non-polar) gases (e.g., chlorine, xenon, krypton, methane, etc.) as well as the hydrates of certain salts (e.g., peralkyl ammonium and sulfonium salts)* now are regarded as essentially solid solutions belonging in the clathrate category (see, for example, Claussen, 1951; Pauling, 1960; Jeffrey, 1962). The stability of the hydrate crystals depends partly upon transient-dipole induced-dipole and permanent-dipole induced-dipole interactions between the entrapped molecules and the framework water molecules and partly upon the energy of the hydrogen bonds.

Since every water molecule forms four hydrogen bonds, the stability of the framework on this account would be expected to be the same as that of ordinary ice, except that it would be diminished slightly because of reduced van der Waals-London interactions between the water molecules in the more open framework (see Pauling, 1961). This is borne out by statistical mechanical calculations which show an increase of free energy over that of ordinary ice at 0°C of only 167 cal / mole for the empty 11.88A clathrate frameworks, such as those which occur in the crystal hydrates of Xe, Cl_2, CH_4, etc. (van der Waals and Platteeuv, 1958). Since the calculated enthalpy increase is only 160 cal / mole (Pauling, 1961), there appears to be little difference in the entropy of water molecules in the empty 11.88A hydrogen-bonded framework and in ordinary ice at 0°C.

Turning now to the stabilization of the hydrate crystals by transient-dipole induced-dipole interactions, Pauling (1961) has calculated an energy value of 10,300 cal / mole for xenon hydrate which, corrected for the enthalpy gain of the water molecules, gives a total stabilization energy relative to ice of roughly 9,400 cal / mole (less a small correction for short-range repulsions). This compares well with the experimental value of 8,400 cal / mole for the enthalpy of formation of $Xe \cdot 5\frac{3}{4}H_2O$ from gaseous xenon and ice at 0°C obtained by von Stackelberg and co-workers (see above).

* In all the peralkylated-cation hydrate structures there is some measure of positional and orientational disorder in the distribution of the cations (within the voids of the host lattice) and of the anions (which are a hydrogen-bonded part of the host lattice) (Beurskens-Kerssen, Jeffrey, and McMullan, 1963).

15

Pauling (1959, 1960) recently suggested that liquid water itself possesses a labile structure, or a range of labile structures, similar to those of the gas and salt hydrates. In this view liquid water can be regarded as a "water hydrate" or an "interstitial solution" consisting of ordered, but highly random, labile frameworks, in which the cages (enclosed regions) are occupied by unbonded water molecules rather than by non-hydrophilic gas molecules.

As a first approximation Pauling suggested a structure involving labile complexes of twenty-one water molecules with icosahedral symmetry (see fig. 5). Twenty of the water molecules would lie at the corners of a pentagonal

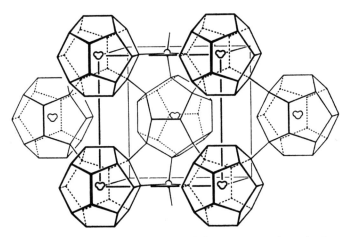

Figure 5. Diagrammatic representation of the structure of gas hydrates containing a hydrogen-bonded framework of 46 water molecules. Twenty molecules, arranged at the corners of a pentagonal dodecahedron, form a hydrogen-bonded complex about the corners of the unit cube, and another 20 form a similar complex, differently oriented, about the center of the cube. In addition there are 6 hydrogen-bonded water molecules, one of which is shown in the bottom face of the cube. In the proposal for the water-hydrate model additional water molecules, not forming hydrogen bonds, occupy the centers of the dodecahedra and also other positions. (Reproduced by courtesy of Dr. L. Pauling and Pergamon Press from Hydrogen Bonding.)

dodecahedron, each participating in three hydrogen bonds with adjacent neighbors in the dodecahedron, one such bond lying along each of the thirty edges of the solid figure. The twenty-first water molecule would form no hydrogen bonds and would occupy the central position inside the dodecahedron, consisting of a cage of about 5A in unobstructed diameter. The dodecahedra may be arranged relative to one another in a large number of ways, forming additional hydrogen bonds with each other or fusing together to share pentagonal faces, and they also may be joined through hydrogen-bonded water-molecule bridges. In addition non-hydrogen-bonded water molecules may be present. Such labile fusing and bridging structures would

16

give rise to fully bonded structures containing other types of "voids"—for example, the inside of a tetrakaidecahedron, which has twelve pentagonal and two hexagonal faces. Such larger "voids" would be of 6A or more free diameter. Structures of this general class have been found to characterize the high hydrates of salts like tetra-isoamyl ammonium fluoride (32 H_2O) and tri-*n*–butyl sulfonium fluoride (20 H_2O) (see Frank and Quist, 1961).

The advantages suggested for the existence of the dodecahedral complex over a tridymite ice-like aggregate of similar size were its stability, as represented by the number of hydrogen bonds that could be formed, and its mobility, while keeping hydrogen bonds formed with surrounding complexes. Thus, the dodecahedral complex contains 71.5% of the maximum number of hydrogen bonds possible, whereas there is no complex of approximately 21 molecules which can be cut out of the tridymite ice structure in which the number of hydrogen bonds is as much as 60% of the maximum possible number (Pauling, 1959).

This water-hydrate structure for liquid water can be regarded as specifying a particular class to which the flickering clusters of Frank and Wen (1957) belong, and it has been analyzed in this light in a statistical-thermodynamic treatment by Frank and Quist (1961). They make the simplifying assumption of a quasi-solid model in which a "snap-shot" of the water sample would show it to be made up solely of clusters; in other words they ignore the presence of molecules (state III) which are neither framework water (state I) nor interstitial water (state II). The numerical application of the analysis is based upon the chlorine-hydrate framework.

In the Frank-Quist analysis of the Pauling model, the equilibrium which is shifted by changes in temperature and pressure is the variable degree of imperfection of the quasi-crystal, i.e., the number of interstitial sites which are left vacant. This latter feature of variable occupancy is, in fact, suggested by the finding (see Frank and Quist, 1961) that an acetone hydrate appears to be able to lose variable amounts of acetone without impairment of the water framework.

The treatment of Frank and Quist (1961) shows that the water-hydrate model can give a satisfactory representation of the P-V-T properties of water, for example the density maximum and "structural compressibility," over limited ranges of temperature and pressure. The entropies and enthalpies derived for the framework and the interstitial water seem physically reasonable, but the simple model (ignoring state III molecules) is less successful in representing the heat capacity* and the partial molal properties of non-polar solutes.

One of the principal findings of the Frank-Quist analysis, emerging from entropy considerations, is that the interstitial, monomer water molecules must be able to rotate freely. This condition appears to be consistent with

---

* The treatment of Némethy and Scheraga (1962a) also encounters difficulties in this domain (see page 13).

other considerations, for the interstitial water molecules should be in rather symmetrical force fields, and studies of the scattering of cold neutrons by liquid water (Hughes, Palevsky, Kley, and Tunkelo, 1960) seem to indicate the existence of freely rotating molecules. Thus, the scattering spectra contain a small peak of energy very slightly lower than that of the incident beam. The shift—about four wave numbers—is a remarkably small one, very nearly equal to the energy difference between the two lowest rotational states of a free water molecule. It is this exchange of such a small amount of sharply quantized energy that indicates the presence of freely rotating molecules.

Essentially unrestricted rotation suggests the interesting possibility that interstitial water molecules become non-hydrophilic, since the dipole moment would tend to be averaged out in most of the rotational states.* Such a condition would accord with von Stackelberg and Müller's (1954) thesis that only non-hydrophilic substances form gas hydrate crystals. As a consequence of the condition of free rotation of interstitial molecules, it follows that the partial molal enthalpy (i.e., the binding) of the monomer-in-its-site must arise from transient-dipole induced-dipole and permanent-dipole induced-dipole interactions.

In addition to accounting for the probable existence of some freely rotating molecules, the Frank-Quist analysis of the water-hydrate model also accounts for other indications of the analyses of cold-neutron scattering, such as the existence of a framework capable of supporting only solid-like, normal modes of vibration. Thus, a large number of neutrons pick up discrete quanta of energy corresponding to the vibrational quanta of known low-frequency Raman bands. The energy presumably is being given up by water molecules engaged in describing one of the normal modes of oscillation which have been ascribed to "hindered rotation" and "hindered translation" (Hughes, Palevsky, Kley, and Tunkelo, 1960; Singwi and Sjölander, 1960; Joshi, 1961).

> The existence of a framework capable of supporting only solid-like, normal modes of vibration is equally well satisfied by the vacant-lattice-point model without the need for additional assumptions. In fact, a simple derivation from the vacant-lattice-point model based upon the "hindered translation" Raman frequency yields the correct value of the diffusion constant (Forslind, 1963). Furthermore, the calculated spectral frequency dependence on the propagation vector for thermal waves in the ice-I lattice shows a very good correlation with the observed spectral distributions in the cold-neutron scattering experiments on water (Forslind, 1963; Larsson and Dahlborg, 1963). Forslind also points out that the theoretical, mean Debye characteristic temperature of about $-163°C$ for the combined longitudinal and transverse modes in ice I is in fairly good agreement (considering the approximate nature of the characteristic temperature concept) with the definitely higher experimental value of $-143°C$ for the water lattice derived from cold-neutron scattering data (see Larsson, Holmryd, and Otnes, 1960).

* But the postulated distribution of monomers over rotational states differs from the normal distribution characteristic of a gas at the same temperature.

The fact that water is a liquid requires a "flickering" character of any framework structure, i.e., that some molecules be in state III (provided that the flow mechanism is restricted to that envisioned by Frank and co-workers). Frank and Quist (1961) suggest that if this third state or group of states, made up of water molecules which have just melted from a cluster and have not yet been incorporated into a new one, were taken into consideration, the shortcomings of the simple model could be overcome. The cold-neutron scattering curves cannot rule out unbonded state-III molecules, since a diffusional effect involving up to 10% of the molecules in cold water and about 25% at 45°C cannot be excluded in a "snap-shot" of roughly 10^{-13} seconds, which is what the cold-neutron scattering experiments give (see Frank and Quist, 1961; Frank, 1963a). Recall, in the latter connection, that the analysis of Némethy and Scheraga (1962a) leads to an expectation of 30% unbonded water molecules at 20°C.

A refinement of the water-hydrate model (more appropriately, of the Samoilov-Forslind model) recently has been proposed by Danford and Levy (1962), whose analysis of the X-ray data seems to rule out the specific, unrefined clathrate structures proposed by Pauling. In their model, water consists of an ice-like framework in which each oxygen atom is surrounded tetrahedrally by four other oxygen atoms in a framework of layers of puckered six-membered rings. Two adjacent layers, related by mirror symmetry, form polyhedral cavities (point symmetry of $\bar{6}m2$) with 12 vertices. The model is accommodated to the required density and distance spectra by the occupation of some of the cavities by lone interstitial water molecules* and by permitting expansion (including anisotropic components) of the framework. A distinctly larger "temperature" coefficient is associated with distances involving interstitial molecules than with other distances.

Each framework oxygen atom has one framework neighbor at 2.77A and three at 2.94A. Each interstitial oxygen atom has three framework neighbors at each of the distances 2.94A, 3.30A, 3.40A, and 3.92A. The ratio of framework molecules to interstitial molecules is 4.0, corresponding to 50% occupancy of the framework cavities. The calculated radial distribution function for this water-hydrate model, in contradistinction to that for an apparently unrefined chlorine-hydrate structure, yields a close fit to the experimentally determined function.

The "distorted-bond" model. According to the liquid water model of Pople (1951), when ice melts the flexibility of the hydrogen bonds becomes greatly increased. Rearrangements of water structure with changes in temperature take place as a result of "bending" or distortion, instead of breaking, of most of the hydrogen bonds. This bending provides a means for extensive absorption of energy and entropy. Bending of the hydrogen bonds is regarded

---

* These were restricted in position to the triad axis and emerged from the analysis off-center along the c-axis.

as a continuously variable rotation of the hydrogen atom, or the lone-pair electrons, or both, out of the O·····O line of centers.

Bending of the hydrogen bonds results in the destruction of the regularly-repeating ice-lattice arrangement, leading to the establishment of an irregular arrangement of the water molecules beyond a few molecular diameters. Accordingly, there is an increase in the number of molecules in the first- and second neighbor shells around a given molecule. This furnishes an explanation for the volume decrease on melting and for the observed increase in coordination number. The radial distributions calculated for different temperatures are in good agreement with the experimental values. In addition the application to the Pople model of the statistical-mechanical theory of the static dielectric constant of polar substances of Harris and Alder (1953), involving a precise evaluation of the distortion polarization, leads to a remarkably accurate calculation (to within 2%*) of the dielectric constant of water from 0 to 83°C. For a discussion of the limitations of the distorted-bond model, see Némethy and Scheraga (1962a).

Numerous other models of liquid water have been proposed (see reviews by Chadwell, 1927; Malenkov, 1962: and also Eucken, 1947, 1948; Hall, 1948; Grunberg and Nissan, 1949; Gierer and Wirtz, 1952; Haggis, Hasted, and Buchanan, 1952; Grjotheim and Krogh-Moe, 1954; van Eck, Mendel, and Fahrenfort, 1958; Ginell, 1961; Mikhailov and Syrnikov, 1960; Namiot, 1961; Wada, 1961; Berendsen, 1962; Gurikov, in Fisher, 1962) but will not be treated here. The models of liquid-water structure discussed in detail above, although able to account for a number of the distinctive features of liquid water, are contradictory in many respects. Accordingly, the problem of liquid water structure must be regarded as being quite unsettled and still in a "work in progress" stage. The Némethy-Scheraga statistical-thermodynamic analysis of the flickering-cluster model is emphasized in the following, since it has the advantages of having been developed most extensively, both quantitatively and qualitatively.

Liquid deuterium oxide. The characteristics of liquid water and deuterium oxide (1.106 g / ml) are very closely similar but there are definite, small differences in the magnitudes of several physical properties (for references see Némethy and Scheraga, 1964). The crystallographic data (Megaw, 1934; Pimentel and McClellan, 1960) indicate that the molecular dimensions and the length of the hydrogen bond are identical to within a few thousandths of an angstrom unit. The fact that the viscosity, the melting point, the tempera-

---

* For comparison, when Kirkwood's (1939) theory of dielectric polarization of polar liquids is applied to liquid water under the assumption of tetrahedral coordination and directed bonds between neighboring molecules, the calculated dielectric constant (Oster and Kirkwood, 1943) deviates from the experimental values (Wyman, 1930) by from -4.3% (0°C) to $+12.7\%$ (83°C). When the Kirkwood theory is applied to the Pople model (Pople, 1951), the deviations are from -18.3% (0°C) to -20.2% (83°C).

ture of maximum density, and the heat capacity of liquid D_2O are higher (Kirshenbaum, 1951), indicates that there is more structural order in liquid D_2O than in liquid H_2O (Némethy and Scheraga, 1964), i.e., that the degree of hydrogen bonding is greater.

The difference in the degree of hydrogen bonding might be attributed to two causes (Némethy and Scheraga, 1964). First, intermolecular vibrational frequencies are lowered by the substitution of the heavier isotope. This results in "looser" hydrogen-bonded structures, i.e., the relative contribution of these structures to the partition function of the liquid is increased, corresponding to a stabilization of them. Second, hydrogen-bonded structures also would be stabilized if the $O—D\cdots O$ bond were stronger than the corresponding $O—H\cdots O$ bond. There are indications that such an increase in bond strength occurs, although the evidence is not conclusive (see Wang, 1951; Pimentel and McClellan, 1960; Scheraga, 1960). The interpretations of recent experiments on deuterium isotope effects lead to contradictory conclusions concerning the relative strengths of hydrogen bonds (involving deuterium or hydrogen) in various systems (see Benjamin and Benson, 1963; Grimison, 1963). However, Némethy and Scheraga (1964) have justified the assumption of stronger $O—D\cdots O$ bonds and have showed that both of the above-mentioned conditions would appear to be required to explain the increased degree of hydrogen bonding in liquid D_2O.

Recently the Némethy-Scheraga (1962a) statistical-thermodynamic analysis of the flickering-cluster model of liquid water has been applied with considerable success to liquid deuterium oxide (Némethy and Scheraga, 1964; see also a treatment by Swain and Bader, 1960). The only adjustable parameter in their treatment is the energy of breaking one hydrogen bond (taken to be 230 cal / mole higher than for H_2O). The intermolecular vibration frequencies were altered in accordance with the theoretical ratios for isotopic substitution.

The results indicated that the size of the clusters, and hence the fraction of the molecules that were inside the clusters, was greater for D_2O than for H_2O at any given temperature. The fraction of unbroken hydrogen bonds also was greater, while the fraction of non-hydrogen-bonded molecules was smaller. For illustration the calculated values of parameters for D_2O are given together with the corresponding values for ordinary water at 20°C (in parentheses). The average-sized cluster consists of 72.4 (57.0) molecules. There are 0.0100 (0.0124) moles of clusters per mole of D_2O. Cluster-members make up 72.7% (70.5) of all molecules, with 27.4% (23.3) quadruply-bonded internally, 17.7% (20.2) triply-bonded, 2.6% (4.1) doubly-bonded, and 25% (23) singly-bonded. In terms of hydrogen bonds remaining unbroken relative to ice, the flickering cluster in D_2O would retain a 48.2% (46.2) ice-like character.

Although the cluster size is considerably greater for D_2O than for H_2O at low temperatures, it decreases much faster with increasing temperature, reflecting the greater degree of structural order existing in D_2O at low temperatures. The breaking down of the structural order of liquid D_2O with increasing temperature must be expected to occur more rapidly than for H_2O, for both forms appear to have similar degrees of order at high temperatures (Wirtz, 1947). The higher heat capacity of D_2O (Eucken and Eigen, 1951) also is consistent with a more rapid breakdown of its structural order.

The computed values of the molar volume at various temperatures were found to be only 0.4% lower than the experimental values (Steckel and Szapiro, 1963), with the relative error decreasing at higher temperatures. Moreover, the temperature dependence was reproduced correctly. In particular, the minimum in the calculated molar volume occurs at 10.2°C—within one degree of the observed value (11.23°C). Since the calculated values were obtained without the use of new assumptions or adjustable factors specific to the application to D_2O, Némethy and Scheraga consider that this derivation provides strong support for the flickering-cluster model of liquid water structure.

The calculated values of the free energy, enthalpy, and entropy of liquid D_2O over the range 0 to 65°C had an over-all average error of 6%, as compared with the experimental data. The deviation of the heat capacity was greater (from +24% at 4°C to +1% at 40°C to −18% at 65°C; see also page 13). Excellent agreement was obtained between the calculated and observed compressibility. The calculated first peak areas for the radial distribution functions of H_2O and D_2O were found to be almost identical. The calculations for D_2O cannot yet be compared with experimental values, for sufficiently detailed X-ray data for D_2O are not available. However, Stewart (1934) stated that the X-ray scattering curves for D_2O and H_2O were almost identical.

ALTERATIONS OF LIQUID-WATER PARAMETERS

Frank-Evans icebergs. An important early attempt to account for the anomalous heats and entropies of solutions of non-polar gases (including noble gases) in water was made by Eley (1939). Eley made use of the concepts developed by Körösy (1937) and Uhlig (1937), according to which the process of dissolving gas molecules in *organic* solvents could be regarded as involving two steps: (1) the formation of cavities in the organic solvent; (2) the transfer of gas molecules from the gas phase into the cavities.

It was proposed that the main contribution to the anomalously high heats of solution (negative enthalpies) of non-polar gases in water relative to those in organic solvents resided in the fact that the energy requirements to form a cavity in water were small. Similarly, the anomalously high negative entropies of solution—about 12 e.u. more negative than in the normal organic solvent—were related to differences in the entropies of cavity formation. Eley pointed out that the displacement of a water molecule by a dissolving non-polar gas molecule, in such a way as to occupy a point in the water

22

quasi-lattice structure, was unlikely considering the large free spaces* in water. For a gas molecule to occupy a water quasi-lattice point would involve the unlikely occurrence of an energy change comparable with the heat of evaporation of water.

Eley suggested instead that interstitial regions of water easily could be enlarged the necessary amount with only a small expenditure of energy because of the possibility of forming structures around the cavity in such a way as to compensate to some extent for the hydrogen bonds broken in the process. The high calculated values of the free volume were consistent with solution occurring into easily formed cavities, whereas if the gas molecules occupied quasi-lattice points of the water, the required entropy changes would have been in disagreement with experiment.

It was concluded (Eley, 1939) that at low temperatures, where the structure of water is important, dissolved non-polar gases occupy certain available interstitial regions, amounting to only about 2% of the total interstitial sites. At higher temperatures,† under which condition water tends to pass into a closely-packed liquid, solution was proposed to occur only onto quasi-lattice points.

Recent correlations of the experimental data with expectations based upon Eley's theory for the various anomalies of aqueous solutions of non-polar gases have led Namiot (1961) to conclude that the magnitude of the enthalpy change when gases dissolve in water can, indeed, be explained upon the basis of Eley's views on the nature of aqueous solutions of non-polar gases. But the specific explanation given by Eley for the considerable decrease of entropy and, consequently, for the low solubility of non-polar gases in water is not consistent with the experimentally established constancy of the activity coefficient at different concentrations of the dissolved gas (Namiot, 1961).

Since the elucidation of the structure of the crystal hydrates of gases, a number of investigators have taken the point of view that, in aqueous solutions of non-polar substances, the solute molecules are contained in cavities analogous to those of the crystalline hydrates (see Claussen and Polglas, 1952; Glew and Robertson, 1956; Malenkov, 1961; Klotz, 1962; Sinanoglu, McKoy, and Abdulner, 1963). The relatively high energetic strength of crystal-hydrate structures provided a plausible explanation for the liberation of heat when non-polar gases are dissolved in water. However, Frank (1963a) has pointed out that the induced ice-likeness cannot consist of clathrate formation in the liquid phase, although the ice-like clusters could be transitory (10^{-11} seconds or longer) fragments of clathrate-like aggregates of pentagonal dodecahedra—particularly in

* Eley (1939) argued that there would be about 9 ml of empty space per mole of water, since closely-packed water molecules would occupy only about 9 ml per mole, i.e., only one-half the volume of a mole of water.

† According to Eley, water starts to behave in a similar way to organic solvents at more normal temperatures (relative to dissolution of non-polar gases), at about 50°C, long before it is closely packed.

view of the finding (see Jeffrey, 1962; Jeffrey and McMullan, 1962; McMullan, Bonamico, and Jeffrey, 1963; Buerskens-Kerssen, Jeffrey, and McMullan, 1963; Beurskens and Jeffrey, 1964) that the variety of detailed structures which can exist in the clathrate category is so much greater than had been imagined previously. Similarly, Namiot (1961), while acknowledging some similarity between clathrates and the ice-likeness induced in aqueous solutions by non-polar compounds, emphasized that significant differences must exist between them in order to account for the low solubility of the non-polar gases.

Eley's (1939) suggestion that the structure of water in the neighborhood of a large non-polar molecule is modified in the direction of closer packing (see also Everett, 1957) implies a reduction in the hydrogen-bonding of the water. In fact Rowlinson (1959), reasoning from purely geometrical considerations, contended that the addition to water of any molecules containing inert groups, such as $-CH_3$, would reduce the total number of hydrogen bonds, even if the inert group itself were attached to a highly polar group. In a similar vein, Forslind (1963), reasoning from recent unpublished nuclear magnetic resonance data, supports the view that non-polar molecules decrease the binding energy of hydrogen bonds in water. However, the prevailing current view, dating from the studies of Frank and Evans (1945), is that the dissolution of a noble-gas atom or a non-polar molecule in water at temperatures in the normal physiological range modifies the water structure in the direction of greater, but still imperfect, crystallinity (Frank and Evans, 1945); i.e., that there occurs an increased degree of hydrogen-bonding or a greater restriction of librational motion of the neighboring water molecules (Powell and Latimer, 1951). A frozen patch, cage, or microscopic "iceberg," which is part of a cluster, tends to form around the non-polar substance, causing enthalpy and entropy to be lost, beyond what would "otherwise" have been expected,* and diminishing the total free volume of the solution. As noted above, the entropy loss per mole of $-CH_2-$ groups of aliphatic chains is approximately 5 to 6 e.u., or 2 to 3 e.u. per mole of water, which is about 40 to 50% of the loss incurred in the formation of the open structure of ordinary ice. This entropy loss is responsible for the increasing insolubility of homologous, long, aliphatic chains of amphiphilic molecules in water.

Frank and Evans (1945) suggested that non-polar molecules or segments of molecules tend to seek out and to occupy regions bordering upon populations of water molecules in which the structure is more open (i.e., more ice-like) and provides more available space. As a result, the open structure might tend to be stabilized and the population of iceberg material increased, possibly with fusion about the non-polar region. The flickering-cluster model of ordinary water now permits a more precise description of this effect.

* For example, highly polar solutes, such as H_2S, NH_3 and SO_2, have partial molal entropies of solution 5 to 10 e.u. more positive than those of comparable non-polar molecules (Powell and Latimer, 1951), implying a large negative "excess of entropy" of the water in solutions of non-polar molecules. Similarly, the enthalpy change, which otherwise is small, becomes large.

According to Frank and Wen (1957), the statistical degree of ice-likeness of water is proportional to the average size and half-life of the clusters. A cluster comes into being when a region undergoes a negative energy fluctuation of such magnitude as to outweigh disruptive influences at its boundaries. It dissolves when these disruptive influences—torques and displacements—transmit the necessary energy of melting into it. Non-polar molecules and saturated hydrocarbon regions of solute molecules are relatively inert insofar as the production or transmission of such disruptive influences is concerned, because of the relative feebleness of their polarizability* and of the electrostatic interactions into which they can enter. Accordingly, ice-like clusters should be able to form more readily in regions bounded by non-polar molecules and, once formed, should have longer half-lives than otherwise by reason of the "boundary protection" received. This postulated lengthening of cluster half-lives tends to be confirmed by the fact that non-polar solutes lengthen the dielectric relaxation times of their aqueous solutions (see Frank, 1958).

In the treatment of Némethy and Scheraga (1962a), the formation of icebergs is placed upon an explicit statistical-thermodynamic basis. The water molecules can be divided into five classes according to their varying energy and internal freedom and depending upon the number of hydrogen bonds in which they are participating. The interiors of the clusters contain quadruply-bonded molecules, whereas their interfaces with unbonded interstitial water contain molecules with one, two, and three hydrogen bonds. The energy level of the quadruply-bonded species is least and is taken as the ground state. Non-polar solute molecules or molecular segments shift the energy levels (and hence the distribution between these levels) of water molecules in the first layer around them, due to different interactions between them and the water.

Water molecules possessing four hydrogen-bonded water neighbors also can have solute neighbors. This increase in coordination number from four to five leads to the depression of the energy level of the quadruply-bonded water molecules below the ground state of pure water, for the fifth neighbor contributes an interaction energy due to permanent-dipole induced-dipole and transient-dipole induced-dipole interactions. On the other hand, unbonded water molecules already have a high coordination number and can acquire a solute neighbor only at the expense of a water neighbor. Since the van der Waals-London interaction between isolated water molecules† is much stronger than it is between water and non-polar solute molecules, the energy levels of non-bonded water molecules are raised. Water molecules with one to three hydrogen bonds, which occur only at the cluster interfaces, also tend to acquire solute neighbors only at the expense of unbonded water neighbors, so that their energy levels also are raised.

---

* For example, the mean polarizability for the C—C bond is only 0.493A^3, as compared to values of 1.33, 1.64, 2.58, and 3.70A^3 for C=O, C=C, C—Cl, and C—Br bonds, respectively (Denbigh, 1940).

† As high as 1000 cal/mole for isolated water dipoles (London, 1937).

As a result of these energy-level changes, there is a net shift of first-layer water molecules from the higher levels into the lower ones, in accord with the Boltzmann distribution law, with a corresponding increase in their ice-likeness. In other words, the net number of water molecules in clusters near the surface of the non-polar molecule is increased. For brevity, these more highly oriented and hydrogen-bonded water molecules in the first layers about non-polar solute molecules are referred to hereafter simply as "icebergs."

For illustration of the effect of iceberg formation on water structure, the calculated hydrogen-bonding in the first water layer around an aliphatic hydrocarbon solute at 20°C is given, together with the corresponding values for ordinary water (in parentheses): fraction of hydrogen bonds unbroken, 59.3% (46.2); quadruply-bonded molecules, 43% (23.3); triply-bonded, 5.9% (20.2); doubly-bonded, 17.6% (4.1); singly-bonded, 12% (23); unbonded, 21.3% (29.5) (Némethy and Scheraga, 1962a).

In addition to their effects on cluster size and stability, non-polar solutes have another effect which has important implications for biological phenomena: the formation and melting of the icebergs bordering these solutes are accompanied by large volume changes. The model of Némethy and Scheraga (1962a) accounts for these changes by the formation and breakdown of incomplete "ice cages" around parts of the non-polar molecules, the extent of the cage depending on the size of the non-polar molecule and the temperature.

The large empty spaces which occur within the hydrogen-bonded framework of ordinary ice also occur in the flickering clusters of liquid water; their persistence is inevitable regardless of the exact structure of the clusters because of the steric restrictions of tetrahedral hydrogen-bonding. Thus, in occupying partial cages on the *borders* of clusters,* regions of the solute molecules fill up part of the space that would be empty in ordinary water clusters, thereby producing a volume decrease. For example, the partial molal volumes of methane and ethane in *n*-hexane are 60 and 69.3 ml, respectively, whereas in water the values fall to 37.3 and 51.2 ml (Gjaldbaek and Hildebrand, 1950; Masterton, 1954). The molar volume for pure benzene is 89.5 ml, but the partial molal volume in aqueous solution is only 83.1 ml.

The magnitudes of the calculated volume decreases for aliphatic chains turn out to be 40 to 60% smaller than those measured experimentally, but this fact does not necessarily reflect a shortcoming of the flickering-cluster concept or its statistical-thermodynamic treatment; part of the observed volume change† may originate from an abnormally high partial molal volume

---

* Namiot (1961) suggests that the low solubility of non-polar molecules in water is to be explained upon the basis of the dissolving molecule interacting, not with all water molecules, but only with clusters.

† Masterton (1954) explained the volume decreases of methane, ethane, propane, and benzene in water in terms of the abnormally high internal pressure of water (12,000 atmospheres as compared to, say, 2,190 atmospheres for *n*-hexane), which was believed to decrease the free volume available to the hydrocarbon molecules.

in non-polar solution. Thus, the partial molal volumes for methane and ethane in non-polar solvents are relatively high compared with their low-temperature liquid volumes (Masterton, 1954).

The thermodynamic instability of icebergs (and clusters) renders them highly sensitive to pressure and temperature changes. The melting of icebergs on temperature increase, in fact, gives rise to enormous partial molal heat capacities (Frank and Evans, 1945). Inasmuch as the volume changes associated with the formation and melting of icebergs are considerable, temperature and pressure changes would be expected to influence strongly any biological processes involving membrane transformations between configurations of markedly different hydration (see chap. 11, vol. II, Kavanau, 1964).

We already have mentioned some of the implications (for membrane structure and transformations) of the tendency of water to form icebergs about the methylene groups of proteins and lipids. At this point it is desirable to emphasize that populations of water molecules having a more ice-like structure will tend to be stabilized in the neighborhood of the methylene groups of all exposed side-chains (whether polar or non-polar) of the protein envelopes.

In concluding the discussion of Frank-Evans icebergs, attention should be called to the theoretical studies of Aranow and Witten (1958, 1960, 1961). The findings of Aranow and Witten are of interest both in connection with the condition of hydrocarbons in the liquid state and with a different interpretation of the interaction between hydrocarbon chains and water molecules in dilute aqueous solution. Their view of the dissolution process seems to be somewhat akin to that of Eley (1939). According to Aranow and Witten (1960), because of the fact that the hydrocarbon chain occupies a cage or cavity in the water structure, the complete rotation of a part of the chain around a C—C bond involves both the relative motion of the parts of the long-chain hydrocarbon molecule and the simultaneous breaking of many hydrogen bonds of the cage surrounding the molecule. Accordingly, complete rotational motion requires high energy and is statistically improbable.

Aranow and Witten (1960) argue that if the shape of the hydrocarbon molecule has a significant effect upon the number of hydrogen bonds in the surrounding cage, it would be reasonable to expect those shapes which permit maximum hydrogen-bonding to correspond to minimum potential energy and, hence, to be preferred. In other words, the molecules of hydrocarbon would tend to assume conformations minimizing the hydrocarbon-water interface. It is postulated that in aqueous solution at room temperature there is one such over-all conformation (or at most a very small number of them), so that the entropy of the hydrocarbon chain is greatly reduced as compared to its entropy when all conformations are allowed.

Thus, as discussed in earlier chapters, the Aranow-Witten model of —CH_2— group behavior permits pseudodegenerate torsional oscillations in organic media (and in non-condensed monolayers at an air-water interface) with many conformations for the molecule as a whole, but requires one preferred conformation for torsional oscillation in aqueous media (and in condensed monolayers and the solid state). While the free energy changes involved in the dissolution of long-chain hydrocarbons in water still are postulated to have an origin primarily in entropy changes, the entropy change of the hydrocarbon chain rather than that of the water is believed to play the major role.

Soft Ice

Ion-dipole oriented water. The term "soft ice" is used here (see also Davies and Rideal, 1961) to designate water that is oriented, bound, and often compressed by polar interactions, as opposed to the water ("icebergs") stabilized about non-polar groups. An ion introduced into water interferes with the quasi-tetrahedral lattice of the water molecules in its neighborhood and tends to impose a new order on them. This is due, to a considerable extent, to the difference between the ion-water and the water-water interactions. Lattice distortions due to purely steric factors (the predominant effect of anions) depend upon the size and shape of the ions. Ions with a crystallographic radius not greater than about 1.3A could be accommodated at the center of an octahedral water shell with very little change in external dimensions (see Benson and Copeland, 1963, and below). Only those ions possessing a smallest radius larger than the radius of the interstitial space distort the lattice for purely geometric reasons (Bergqvist and Forslind, 1962). The larger the volume of a dissolved ion, the greater is the steric disturbance and the more extensive is the zone in which hydrogen bonds are being disturbed or broken.

On the other hand, interactions between the solute and the water lattice give rise to additional lattice distortions (most marked for cations) associated with changes in the ionic and molecular charge distributions.* The nearest-neighbor water molecules of ions not larger than Cs^+ and I^-, for example, generally are regarded as being immobilized, strongly polarized, and highly compressed by ion-dipole† and other interactions with the large electrical fields (of the order of 10^6 to 10^7 V / cm) in the vicinity of the ions (Bernal and Fowler, 1933; Eley and Evans, 1938; Verwey, 1942; Frank and Evans, 1945; Gurney, 1953; Shoolery and Alder, 1955; Frank and Wen, 1957; Samoilov, 1957b; Bergqvist and Forslind, 1962).

Transition-metal ions can form strong donor-acceptor bonds with water and, accordingly, can distort the structure of water substantially (usually forming octahedral complexes). The attraction between these ions and water

---

* Samoilov (1957b) divides the non-steric effects into: (1) a possible difference between the coordination numbers of the ion and the water molecule; and (2) reorientation of the water molecules closest to the ion.

† The interaction energy is roughly 5,000 cal / mole of bound water (Dole and McLaren, 1947). The mobility of the water molecules nearest to the ion is not believed to be related directly to the ion-water interaction energy, but apparently depends only upon the variations of the energy with distance at small distances (Samoilov, 1957a).

is so strong that complexes can be identified in solution. A well-known case is that of $[Cr(H_2O)_6]^{3+}$, where the exchange rate of the complexed water molecules is known to be very slow, their half-life being about 40 hours (Hunt and Taube, 1951). The half-life of the single water molecule in $[Co(NH_3)_5H_2O]^{3+}$ is about 24.5 hours. The exchange rate for other trivalent ions is too rapid to detect by the O^{18} tracer technique, indicating a half-life of less than three minutes.

Nuclear magnetic resonance (NMR) studies of paramagnetic cations, involving measurements of the resonance signals from O^{17}-enriched water (see below), give mean lifetimes of water molecules in the first coordination sphere ranging from 5×10^{-7} seconds for Cu^{2+} to 3.7×10^{-3} seconds for Ni^{2+}. The enthalpy of activation for the exchange of these water molecules with bulk water is 5,000 to 11,600 cal / mole (Swift and Connick, 1962). For Be^{2+}, NMR studies give a mean lifetime of roughly 3×10^{-4} seconds and a hydration number of roughly four (Connick and Fiat, 1963).

For the alkali-metal cations, systematic measurements of the substitution of several first-hydration-shell water molecules by ligands have been carried out recently by sound absorption techniques (see Eigen, 1963). The substitution rate constants, which probably also give a rough measure of the water-water exchange rates, vary from 0.47 to 9.0×10^8 per second for Li^+ to from 2.1 to 50×10^8 per second for Cs^+, depending upon the ligand (EDTA, nitrilotriacetate, iminodiacetate, and polyphosphates). For the alkaline-earth cations, relaxation techniques (sound absorption, fast spectrophotometric rates, and the dispersion of the dissociation field effect) give rates for water substitution for various ligands of from 10^5 per second for Mg^{2+} to about 5×10^8 per second for Ba^{2+} (see Eigen, 1961, 1963). It is striking that the rate for Ca^{2+} is about one thousand times greater than that for Mg^{2+}. Radically different exchange rates between first-hydration-sphere water and bulk water for Ca^{2+} and Mg^{2+} also are indicated by studies of self-diffusion and by the temperature coefficients of the ion mobilities in solution. Thus, the activation energy for the exchange of nearest-neighbor water molecules is only 450 cal / mole for Ca^{2+} as opposed to 2,610 cal / mole for Mg^{2+} (Samoilov, 1955, 1957a). The magnitudes of the exchange rates indicated above should be kept in mind in the subsequent discussions of "immobilization" of nearest-neighbor water molecules by ionic solutes.

The effect of an ion on water structure is roughly proportional to its polarizing power, i.e., to its charge divided by its radius. Ion-oriented water forms a rather rigid crust, the shear surface generally being thought to be extended by at least the thickness of one molecule. In the case of alkylammonium and carboxylate ions, for example, the range of influence on neighboring water molecules has been estimated experimentally at 5A (Everett, 1957).

Dielectric polarization, immobilization, and compression of water molecules by the ionic field lead to a large gain of potential energy and to large entropy and volume decreases. But in contrast to the large increase in heat capacity caused by icebergs, the restrictions placed upon solvent molecules around ions lead to a substantial decrease in the heat capacity (both thermal and configurational) of the solution (the ions have large, negative, partial molar heat capacities at infinite dilution). The ionization of water to one mole each of H_3O^+ and HO^- ions, both of which become strongly hydrated, entails a unitary entropy loss of 35 e.u. (Rossini, 1952) and a volume reduction of 21 ml (Linderstrøm-Lang and Jacobsen, 1941), these changes reflecting the polarization, immobilization, and electrostriction* of a considerable number of neighboring water molecules. The strength of the specific interaction between protons and water molecules is indicated by the fact that the heat of hydration of a proton (276,000 cal / mole) greatly exceeds that of any other monovalent ion (being 145,000 cal / mole greater than that of Li^+) and far exceeds the heat of dissociation of water (13,336 cal / mole), suggesting the existence of a valence bond between the proton and a water molecule (see Richards and Smith, 1951; Eigen and De Maeyer, 1958, 1959).

It is appropriate at this point to consider the problem of dielectric saturation of water in the neighborhood of an ion, a phenomenon for which no definitive theory yet exists. The first attempt to provide a theory of the dielectric constant of polar liquids at high field strengths was made by Debye (1929), but his treatment now is known to be invalid. Onsager (1936) provided a much better but oversimplified theory. The deviation of the local polarization from the average was taken into account by treating the molecule as a real cavity in a statistical continuum of uniform dielectric constant equal to that of the liquid in bulk. With this model and the macroscopic electrostatic theory of continuous media, the local field and average torque effective in orienting a dipolar molecule relative to an external field could be calculated readily. Kirkwood (1939) extended the Onsager theory, giving a general analysis for hydrogen-bonded liquids. He assumed hindered rotation of the neighbors of a dipolar molecule relative to the molecule, due to short-range intermolecular forces, and he approximated the local dielectric constant by the macroscopic dielectric constant of the fluid in a region outside a molecule and its first shell of neighbors (rather than in the entire region exterior to the molecule). However, both the Onsager and Kirkwood treatments were confined to cases involving relatively low field strengths. Booth (1951, 1955) generalized the Onsager and Kirkwood treatments to obtain expressions for the dielectric constant at high field strengths. He showed that the reduction in its value due to the saturation effect is important for fields greater than about 10^6 volts/cm, but his method depends upon several simplifying assumptions.

The problem also has been treated by Schwarzenbach (1936), Ritson and Hasted (1948), Grahame (1950), Bolt (1954, 1955), Buckingham (1957), Schellman (1957), Noyes (1962), and Padova (1963). Schwarzenbach's results lead to an effective dielectric constant of water between two isolated monovalent ions separated by 5 to 10A of roughly nineteen to forty-nine (Pressman, Grossberg, Pence, and Pauling, 1946). The theory of Ritson and Hasted predicts a region

* The electrostriction in an electrolyte solution is defined as the change in total volume taking place during the dissolution of one mole of electrolyte in a large volume of solute.

30

of complete dielectric saturation up to about 2A from a point electronic charge, where the dielectric constant has a value of four to five. This is followed by a region of rapid rise to the ordinary bulk value at about 4A. Thus, nearly all the lowering of the dielectric constant would arise from effects in the primary hydration shell (see also Buckingham, 1957). First-hydration saturation is regarded as complete only for cations, whereas the Kirkwood (1939) and Booth (1951, 1955) analyses assumed complete ordering for nearest-neighbors about both anions and cations. According to Grahame's (1950) analysis, the dielectric constant does not begin to drop sharply until a distance of approach of about 4A from the center of a monovalent ion; it then drops rapidly to a value of about twenty at 2A and to a value of less than five at 1A. The analysis by Bolt indicates that the dielectric constant remains virtually constant from infinity up to approximately 5A from the center of a monovalent ion. It then drops off very sharply to a low value of three to six.

Using an improved method for evaluating changes in thermodynamic properties associated with the hydration of individual species of gaseous monatomic ions, Noyes (1962) has calculated the effective properties of the solvent in the neighborhood of the ions. A surprising, in fact almost unbelievable, result emerged. For cations having the noble-gas electronic structure the free energies of hydration indicated effective dielectric constants that were linearly related to the crystallographic radii of the ions and virtually independent of charge. For example, the local dielectric constant varied from 1.389 for Be^{2+} (radius = 0.31A) to 3.228 for Cs^+ (radius = 1.69A). According to Noyes, during the reversible charging of an initially neutral molecule, a small fraction of an electronic charge polarizes the surrounding solvent molecules and causes a reduced local dielectric constant, while continued charging even to three electronic units would seem to have very little further influence upon it. In connection with these unexpected results of Noyes's (which are so much at variance even with the simple Debye-Hückel theory) one should bear in mind that they hinge upon the validity of the Born model for ion-water interactions. Since such purely electrostatic approaches involve a number of assumptions and uncertainties (see page 66), these results should perhaps be regarded with reservations.

In spite of the internal consistency of Noyes's (1962) data, they cannot be extrapolated with enough confidence to distinguish between two models for the decrease in the dielectric constant with distance. According to one of these models the local dielectric constant would rise to its value in bulk water at 2.86A from the center of a cation, while according to the other, the limit would be reached at 113A. A choice between the two models would seem to require data for larger cations.

Padova (1963, 1964) recently has found it possible to apply the thermodynamic treatment of a fluid in an electrostatic field to the problem of calculating various properties of electrolyte solutions at infinite dilution, assuming the solvent to be under the influence of the electric field caused by the presence of the ions. According to his calculations the dielectric constant about small monatomic ions is constant (at a low value) and independent of field strength at a distance up to 1.80A from the center of the ion. At greater distances the dielectric constant rises, attaining the bulk value at 8A, also independently of field strength.

Hydrogen-bonded and dipole-dipole oriented water

HYDROGEN-BONDED WATER. Orientation of water molecules by the highly directional hydrogen bond (large positive ΔV) should play an important role in connection with both un-ionized groups on polar side-chains of the protein envelopes and un-ionized, polar, lipid head-groups, most of which are capable of being either hydrogen-bond donors or receivers. The competition of hydrogen-bonding to water molecules, in fact, renders the net strength of hydrogen bonds between polar residues in an aqueous environment rather small, reducing the enthalpy of formation to only $-1,500$ cal / mole (see Némethy, Steinberg, and Scheraga, 1963).

Two significant features of the water molecule are: (1) it is so small that it can fit into quite small interstices in proteins (Coulson, 1957), in the water lattice itself (Samoilov, 1946; Forslind, 1952; Pauling, 1959), and in the lipid-protein interfacial region of biological membranes; and (2) it has the power both to give and to receive hydrogen bonds. Although large deviations of hydrogen bonds from linearity are not allowed because of their partially covalent character, it is not necessary for the hydrogen bonds to be absolutely straight (Pople, 1951; Coulson, 1957; Donohue, 1957; Cannon, 1958; Bacon, 1959), particularly in the case of long, weak hydrogen bonds. This fact is of great importance in connection with the fitting of water molecules into small spaces.

Hydrogen-bonding is inevitable wherever peptide links occur; it is particularly important in the unfolded state of proteins, in which condition the peptide groups are most free to interact. Under the most favorable conditions, four molecules of water could be bound by each peptide group (Sponsler, Bath, and Ellis, 1940), but mutual hydrogen-bonding competes strongly with hydrogen-bonding of water and is overwhelmingly predominant in the interior of globular proteins* (see, for example, Kendrew, 1962, 1963; Tanford, 1962). There can, of course, be no water in the interior of the α-helix (see Némethy, Steinberg, and Scheraga, 1963).

Jacobson (1953a) has suggested that the interstitial volume in an ideal water lattice based upon the ice-I lattice (fig. 3) can be visualized as having a spatial arrangement like that of helices parallel to the *a*-axis (fig. 6). Helices of different dimensions were proposed with pitches of $4.74n$ A (at 25°C), where n is the number of water-lattice units in the *a*-axis direction (i.e., n times the second-nearest-neighbor distance in any water lattice based upon the tetrahedral angle).

Jacobson speculated that if a cylindrical or helical section of water were to be removed from the ideal water lattice parallel to the *a*-axis, a cavity would be formed, the surface of which would have oxygen atoms arranged in a helical manner similar to that of the interstitial helical space. These oxygen atoms presumably would be free to form hydrogen bonds with a macro-

---

* A few single water molecules may be trapped at the time the molecules are folded (Kendrew, 1962, 1963).

molecule fitting into the cavity. Jacobson (1953a) further speculated that the Watson-Crick DNA double-helix might fit well into cavities in this water lattice,* for the repeating distance along a DNA helix equals seven a-axis repeating distances. In this connection, the studies of Hearst and Vinograd

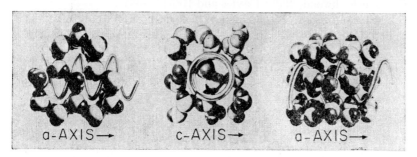

a-AXIS→   c-AXIS→   a-AXIS→

Figure 6. Scale molecular model of the ideal water lattice based upon the ice-I lattice showing in a purely schematic way how a DNA helix might be visualized as integrating into the lattice. (Reproduced by courtesy of Dr. B. Jacobson.)

(1961) indicate that T-4 bacteriophage CsDNA molecules (at 25°C) have about 50 water molecules of hydration per nucleotide residue at water activity near unity.

That a relationship similar to that proposed by Jacobson exists between collagen and water has been asserted by Berendsen (1960, 1962). The repeating distance of 28.6A along the axis of the collagen helix equals six a-axis repeats of the ideal water lattice within an accuracy of 2% for the temperature range from 17 to 38°C. Berendsen suggests that the collagen macromolecules stabilize chains and possibly three-dimensional structures of water molecules (with tetrahedral angles between the bonds) in the hydration crust by the formation of hydrogen bonds at appropriate positions. Berendsen's (1962) proton magnetic resonance results can be explained if the chains of water molecules form parallel to the fiber axis and rotate or reorient about their long axis. Such chains would be hydrogen-bonded extensively to any collagen molecules that could form hydrogen bonds to water in the appropriate directions. Since the lifetime of an individual chain would be fairly short, the breaking and reforming of hydrogen bonds within the chains and between the collagen and the water molecules would provide a mechanism for chain rotation.

DIPOLE-DIPOLE ORIENTED WATER. Orienting and binding of water molecules by the weaker dipole-dipole interactions probably predominate in regions of membranes containing un-ionized polar groups incapable of hydrogen-bonding

---

* Of course, the macromolecules first would disrupt the water structure—an action which could conceivably be followed by structural reorganization, leaving the macromolecules in closely-fitting helical cavities. Note, however, that Jacobson ignores the effects of the strong local electric fields near the phosphate groups and the structure-modifying influences of other portions of the macromolecule.

for either constitutive or steric reasons and may compete to a significant degree even in regions where hydrogen-bonding occurs. The dipoles of monolayer-forming molecules may orient and hinder the rotation of the dipoles of several layers of water molecules at the interface below the head groups (see Kirkwood, 1957; Davies and Rideal, 1961).

LONG-RANGE ORIENTATION OF WATER. When the interface of a substance with a liquid is built up of individual molecules held together by relatively weak forces, which permit slight deviations from strict crystalline periodicity of a molecular array (as, for example, in monolayers and micelles), the equilibrium configuration at the interface generally will be determined jointly by the structure of the two phases (see Hazlehurst and Neville, 1940). Hardy (1927) and McBain and Davies (1927) independently suggested that the tendency of anisotropic molecules in bulk liquids to take up orderly arrangements (cybotaxis) might be reinforced and developed strongly by proximity to such interfaces, the action being relayed away from the interface, thus giving rise to chains of solvent (and solute) molecules (see also Ostwald, 1928; Hauser, 1931; Freundlich, 1932). Derjaguin and his collaborators (Derjaguin, 1936; Derjaguin and Titijevskaya, 1957; Derjaguin and Karassev, 1957) have found that liquid films in contact with a glass or a mica surface seem to be rigidified to a depth of 1,000 to 1,500A.

Forslind (1952, 1953) has shown that coupling between water and a clay crystal imparts an increased order and rigidity to the water lattice (thermal vibrations in the lattice being reduced) which apparently can be effective at distances of at least 300A (see also Bernal, 1959). The rigidity of the adsorbed water lattice is believed to drop off exponentially with distance from the interface (Macy, 1952). Coupling between water and an interface can be more or less specific, depending upon the degree of structural similarity between the ideal water lattice (figs. 3 and 6) and the stabilizing interface. Forslind suggested that gel formation and the apparent existence of long-range interactions in gel-forming systems were the consequences of specific adsorption of water at the interface with the colloid. In the same vein, Winsor (1954) proposed that the interstitial water molecules in aqueous mesophases might be ordered into specific quasi-crystalline arrangements under the influence of the regularly disposed, polar head-groups of the amphiphiles (see also Dervichian, 1946).

These views were extended by Jacobson (1955) who proposed that macromolecular interfaces stabilize surrounding water into lattice-ordered hydration shells (fig. 7), which may build up and break down slowly. According to Jacobson, certain of the physical properties of aqueous solutions of polar colloids, like those of non-polar solutes, might be caused partly or mainly by structural changes in the water lattice, rather than solely by the specific properties of the macromolecules (see also Hammarsten, 1924). It was proposed that the hydration shells are ice-like, in the sense that thermal vibrations in the lattice are reduced and that the number of Frenkel lattice defects are fewer than the number in water. However, Jacobson pointed out that lone interstitial water molecules would give the lattice about the same density as that of normal water, and that the thermodynamic properties of the hydration shells probably would resemble water more than ice. In the latter connection, the dielectric dispersions of solutions of macromolecules that give dielectric increments fall in the range between the dielectric dispersions of ice and water.*

The lattice order in the hydration shells envisioned by Jacobson was expected to decrease with distance from the interface with the macromolecule. If many oxygen and nitrogen atoms at the interface of the macromolecule were in positions such that they could fit into the ideal water lattice, a very pronounced ordering of the water would be expected—one resulting in an almost ideal four-coordinated structure (fig. 7). On the other hand, if the hydrogen-bonding atoms were in positions such that bonding with the water lattice were hindered, no ordering effect would be expected, and the water

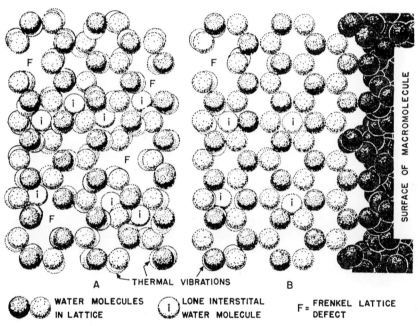

A   THERMAL VIBRATIONS   B

WATER MOLECULES   LONE INTERSTITAL   F = FRENKEL LATTICE
IN LATTICE   WATER MOLECULE   DEFECT

Figure 7. Diagrammatic representation of the ordering of water in the vicinity of a macromolecule by those of its exposed oxygen and nitrogen atoms that fit into the ideal water lattice (as proposed by Jacobson). A, the bulk water; B, ordered water having fewer Frenkel lattice defects and reduced amplitudes of thermal vibrations compared to the bulk water. (Reproduced by courtesy of Dr. B. Jacobson and the American Chemical Society.)

* Water has a dielectric dispersion at 10^{10} cycles / sec, while that of ice occurs at 10^2 to 10^4 cycles / sec, depending on the temperature (see Auty and Cole, 1952).

lattice probably would be unchanged or would become even more disordered. The shape and absolute size of the macromolecule were suggested to be of importance in determining its capacity to order a large volume of water far from its interface.

According to this view, the solubility of a macromolecule and its effect on the viscosity of the solution would be determined partly by its relative hydrogen-bonding capacity for the solute (i.e., by its "fit" with the water lattice). If the capacity were small compared to that of intermolecular hydrogen bonding, the substance probably would be insoluble; if the capacity were large (as for DNA), the substance would be miscible with water in all proportions and the viscosity of the solution would be relatively high. If large amounts of water were immobilized (causing gel formation), the dissolution process might be very slow.

Jacobson's theory originally was developed to explain the dielectric properties of solutions of macromolecules (Jacobson, 1953a, 1953b; Jacobson and Laurent, 1954). Thus, the hypothesis that the dielectric properties of macromolecular solutions arise to a great degree as a result of the formation of lattice-ordered hydration shells, rather than from rotations of whole molecules with fixed electric moments, appeared to be capable of explaining qualitatively many of the experimental dielectric observations. However, the theory also helped to interpret viscosity and osmotic pressure data and the X-ray scattering and pioneering proton magnetic resonance findings for DNA solutions (Jacobson, Anderson, and Arnold, 1954; Jacobson, 1955). The latter two experimental techniques had indicated that the structure of water was affected markedly by the presence of certain macromolecules.

Jacobson's theory stimulated widespread interest in the problem of macromolecular hydration. But in spite of much subsequent experimentation the questions of the nature and degree of the influence exerted on water structure by *certain* dissolved macromolecules and, particularly, by micellar interfaces remain unsettled. Conductivity and nuclear magnetic resonance data at first tended to support Jacobson's views. In concentrated solutions of gelatin at high field strengths the electrical conductivity suggested ordering of the water molecules by the protein molecules to give the water properties similar to those of ice (Ril, 1955). Mays and Brady (1956) found that water molecules adsorbed on solid TiO_2 became immobilized when the coverage attained a complete monolayer. At higher coverages the proton resonance line width suggested an ice-like structure.

However, from studies of the self-diffusion coefficient of water in aqueous NaDNA solutions (as a function of concentration), Wang (1955) computed that the water of hydration amounted to only 0.35 gram per gram of dry NaDNA.* In Wang's view this degree of hydration was too low to allow the proton magnetic resonance findings of Jacobson, Anderson, and Arnold (1954)

* For comparison, the same method gives a value of only 0.18 gram per gram of dry protein for the hydration of ovalbumin (see also below) in its isoelectric salt-free solution (Wang, 1954a).

36

to be interpreted entirely in terms of a simple hydration effect. This note of discord was followed shortly by another. Laurent (1957) found that the hydration of hyaluronic acid in solution in concentrations below 2% produced only insignificant changes in the X-ray scattering spectra. This led him to conclude that for hyaluronic acid, at least, X-ray scattering gave no evidence of large hydration shells with an increased four-coordinated hexagonal lattice structure.

Before continuing with a discussion of the nuclear magnetic resonance (NMR) findings concerning long-range orientation of water, a brief introductory summary of some of the parameters of these studies is given. Detailed accounts are to be found in the works of Jackman (1959), Pople, Schneider, and Bernstein, (1959), Roberts (1961), and Jardetzky and Jardetzky (1962a, 1962b). The following account is drawn in large part from the treatments of Jardetzky and Jardetzky.

The phenomenon of nuclear magnetic resonance occurs only in the case of atomic nuclei possessing angular momentum and, therefore, a nuclear magnetic moment; it is most frequently observed in diamagnetic* compounds. Both the angular momentum and the nuclear magnetic moment are vector quantities which assume definite quantized directions with respect to a stationary external magnetic field. Each such orientation with respect to the stationary external field is characterized by a potential energy. Transitions between adjacent orientations or potential energy levels can occur by absorption of circularly-polarized radio-frequency electromagnetic radiation which arises from a second weak magnetic field rotating in a plane perpendicular to the axis of the stationary magnetic field.

The principal feature of the NMR spectra is the dependence of the resonance frequency upon the electronic environment surrounding the nucleus as well as upon the chemical nature of the nuclear species. Experimental techniques permitting the resolution of individual lines in the resulting complex spectra are referred to collectively as high resolution NMR spectroscopy. In wide-line or broad-band NMR spectroscopy, information is derived from the characteristics of a single broad line (as observed primarily in solids and minimally-solvated material).

The NMR signal can be characterized by: (1) its width, which usually is measured at half-height in frequency units; (2) its total (integrated) intensity, i.e., the area under the absorption curve; and (3) its position on a frequency scale. The width of the resonance line from a water proton, for example, is proportional to the correlation time, τ_c, which sets a time scale for the random motion of the protons. This time is of the order of the time it takes for a water molecule to turn through a radian, or to move through a distance comparable with its dimensions. Any change in the water structure is expected to be reflected in a change in the correlation time and, hence, in the line width. The correlation

---

* If the magnetic field intensity in a region inside of matter placed between the two poles of a magnet is less than the field intensity *in vacuo*, the substance is termed *diamagnetic;* substances in which the field intensity is greater than *in vacuo* are termed *paramagnetic*. The reduction of the effective field, at a given nucleus in diamagnetic substances, to a value somewhat lower than the applied field is referred to as *shielding*.

time of liquid water at 20°C (as deduced from dielectric measurements) is about 3×10^{-12} seconds, corresponding to a theoretical NMR line width of about 0.05 milligauss (Wertz, 1955). However, the line width also is a measure of the magnetic field inhomogeneity over the sample; even with stringent precautions to reduce the residual inhomogeneity, it is extremely difficult to reach this figure.

The area under a resonance signal, since it is proportional to the number of resonating nuclei (in the absence of saturation of the sample), can serve as a measure of the total number of particles of a given type present in the sample. However, one usually is confined to the much simpler procedure of measuring the relative numbers of particles in different sets of nuclei by comparing areas under two different absorption curves. But if a narrow line is superimposed upon a broad one it may not be possible to obtain a quantitative comparison of the nuclei in the two states because the different line breadths require different experimental conditions for their accurate measurement.

The interpretation of high resolution spectra depends to a considerable extent on determinations of line position. The position of the resonance line from a proton in a water molecule is dependent upon the magnetic field at the resonating proton, which is the vector sum of the applied field and any additional fields that may be produced by the surroundings. Thus, a change in either the applied magnetic field or the local magnetic field results in a shift in the line position. Customarily the position of a line is specified relative to the position of an arbitrary standard line. The separation between the peaks of two absorption lines is called *the shift*. Four types of shifts can be distinguished according to the underlying physical mechanism:

    1) the diamagnetic or chemical shift;*

    2) the paramagnetic shift in solutions;

    3) the Knight shift, or the paramagnetic shift in metals; and

    4) shifts resulting from interactions between nuclei, the simplest of these being a splitting of the absorption lines.

When the electron environments around protons (or other nuclei of the same kind) are different at different sites in a molecule, signals of different Larmor frequencies are received from the non-equivalent protons at the different sites. It is the separations between these different signals that are referred to as chemical shifts. These shifts have their origin to large degree in the diamagnetic and paramagnetic shielding effects produced by the circulation of both bonding and non-bonding electrons in the neighborhoods of the nuclei. In addition to the correlation of the chemical shift to the existence of intramolecular electronic currents and to the character and number of bonds in which the atoms participate, the magnitude of the shift is affected by: (1) the electronegativity of a substituent;† (2) the magnetic anisotropy of neighboring atoms or groups

---

* Relative chemical shifts can be expressed in units of frequency (cycles per second = cps), in magnetic field units (gauss), or in dimensionless units (parts per million). In the recent literature the shifts are measured almost exclusively in the latter units.

† Electron-withdrawing groups such as —OH, —NH₂, and ⟍C=O shift the resonance peaks to lower fields when they are substituents on open-chain compounds, but have the opposite effect when they are substituents in aromatic systems.

(especially the circulation of electrons in ring systems); and (3), the participation of the proton-bearing group in one or more resonating structures of the molecule. Unless one can take into account adequately the individual contributions to a shift, the interpretation of the shift is difficult.

In the exchange of protons from one electron environment to another, there is an accompanying switch of the resonance frequency of the protons to different values. Accordingly, it is possible to "track" the exchange reaction because the protons are "labeled" by their Larmor frequency. Experimentally, one determines the increase in the line width in the NMR spectrum caused by these frequency changes.

The qualitative changes observed in the NMR spectrum of a system as its exchange rate is increased gradually from zero to a high value are as follows: Initially one observes a gradual broadening of the resonance lines involved in the exchange. This broadening has been termed "lifetime broadening" (Meiboom, 1961) because it can be considered to result from the finite time a nucleus stays in a definite frequency state. The broadening increases at higher exchange rates until the individual lines overlap and result in a single broad line. On continued increase of the exchange rate, the individual resonance frequencies begin to average and the line narrows, until, at very fast rates, a single sharp line is observed (at the center of gravity of the contributing lines). The stage in which there is a single collapsed line is referred to as "exchange narrowing."

The possibility of applying proton-resonance measurements to the study of hydrogen-bonding became apparent following the observation by Arnold and Packard (1951) that the position of the proton signal of the —OH group in the spectrum of ethyl alcohol was temperature and concentration dependent—shifting to a higher field with increase of temperature and increasing dilution in an inert solvent, and to a lower field with decrease of temperature and increasing concentration. This behavior of the —OH signal was attributed to hydrogen-bonding (Liddel and Ramsey, 1951). Shifts due to hydrogen-bonding are termed "hydrogen-bond" chemical shifts or "association" shifts to distinguish them from ordinary chemical shifts. They represent in fact a shift of the chemical shift (Schneider, 1959).

The resonance peak of hydrogen-bonded protons appears at lower fields than the peak of non-hydrogen-bonded protons attached to the same atom (see Liddel and Ramsey, 1951; Huggins, Pimentel, and Shoolery, 1955; Pople, 1959; Schneider, 1959; Pimentel and McClellan, 1960). This is a direct result of a lowering of the effective electron density at the proton by electrostatic interaction (i.e., a decrease in diamagnetic shielding). The association shifts of substances forming strong hydrogen bonds are believed to be distinctly larger than the shifts of other substances (see Pimentel and McClellan, 1960). Whereas the interaction of the two protons in a structurally-bound water molecule may result in line shifts of many gauss (Pake, 1948), the hydrogen-bonded structure of liquid water produces shifts only of the order of milligauss (Hindman, 1962).

The various types of radiationless transitions by which a nucleus in an upper spin state returns to a lower state are called *relaxation processes*. These may be divided into the two categories of *spin-lattice (longitudinal) relaxation* and *spin-spin (transversal) relaxation*. In spin-lattice relaxation the energy of the nuclear spin system is converted into thermal energy of the entire molecular system containing the magnetic nuclei (i.e., the environment or "lattice"), and is therefore directly responsible for maintaining the unequal distribution of spin states. In the spin-spin relaxation process a nucleus in its upper spin state transfers its energy to a neighboring nucleus of the same isotope by a mutual exchanging of spin, a process which does not require spin-lattice energy transfer. Either or both of these relaxation processes may control the natural line width.

The efficiency of, or time required for, spin-lattice relaxation can, like other exponential processes, be expressed in terms of a finite characteristic time called the spin-lattice or longitudinal relaxation time T_1. Operationally this is defined as the time required for the Boltzmann distribution to be established (with respect to the z-axis, i.e., the axis of the magnet) in the perturbed system of nuclei resulting from placing the sample in the magnetic field (usually 10^{-3} to 20 seconds for liquids). Fundamentally, spin-lattice relaxation is produced by oscillating local magnetic fields* which induce transitions in much the same way as the rotating field. The shortening of T_1 is proportional to the intensity of the local magnetic fields which may be oscillating at the Larmor precession frequency in the sample. Since the spin-lattice relaxation time is inversely proportional to the correlation time for liquids that are not exceptionally viscous, it gives an independent measure of proton mobility.

The transverse relaxation time, T_2, is characteristic of relaxation in the plane perpendicular to the z-axis. It can be interpreted as the average time required for two nuclei to get out of phase as a result of spin-spin relaxation. For a Lorentzian line,† the transverse relaxation time is related to the full width at half-amplitude in cycles per second, Δ, by the relation, $\Delta = 1/\pi T_2$ (see Meiboom, 1961). The most widely used technique for measuring T_2 is known as the "spin-echo" method. Both T_1 and T_2 are influenced by hydrogen-bonding.

Unlike the direct magnetic dipole-dipole interaction between nuclei, the spin-spin interaction is not removed by random reorientations of the molecules. Spin-spin coupling between the magnetic moments of two or more protons of the same molecule alters the effective magnetic field experienced by the protons and leads to a splitting of their resonance lines into two or more components.

Reviewing first the studies of Jacobson, Anderson, and Arnold (1954), it was found that the resonance signals from the water protons were broadened and that the area beneath the curves was decreased by NaDNA solutions but not by solutions of hemocyanin, starch, or ovalbumin. The fraction of the water protons having a signal width of greater than 15 milligauss (the width for pure water was found to be 3 milligauss) increased from 0.06 to 0.85 as the DNA concentration was increased from 6% to 60% by weight. Several causes for this remarkable line broadening were suggested, including increased order of the water lattice and exchanging of protons or water molecules (see page 74) between ordered and disordered phases of the water.

* For protons and other nuclei of spin $\frac{1}{2}$, the only way in which the nuclear spin can be coupled with other degrees of freedom is by means of local fluctuating magnetic fields.

† The Lorentzian shape (i.e., a Lorentz-type curve; see Jardetzky and Jardetzky, 1962b) of the magnetic resonance line is an approximation valid only under the special circumstance of both the conditions of steady state and of very low oscillator intensity being satisfied experimentally.

This pioneering study is now of primarily historical interest. One reason is that it suffered from a lack of definition of possibly pertinent instrumental variables. The observed decrease in area subsequently was shown to be an instrumental artifact (see Williams, 1958). Another reason is that the line width probably was determined by phase inhomogeneities, possibly including the presence of microscopic air bubbles in the solution—now a well-recognized source of error. Thus, the findings probably bore little or no relation to hydration. Studies of the next six years (see below and above) suffered to varying degrees from the same deficiencies.

Jardetzky and Jardetzky (1957) found the width of the proton-resonance line of 1.9% solutions of tobacco mosaic virus to be increased by about 25% over that for pure water. The broadening was suggested to be caused by the average dipole-dipole interactions between the protons of oriented and free water. Similarly, the line-width increases in solutions of fibrous materials found by Odajima, Sohma, and Watanabe (1959) were attributed to water adsorption. Resonance signals from certain cell preparations also were found to be broadened (Odeblad, 1959).

Balazs, Bothner-By, and Gergely (1959) found that 2% DNA solutions gave a marked broadening of the water proton signal. No changes whatsoever were observed in the signals given by solutions of collagen, hyaluronic acid, gelatin, or myosin. Accordingly, it was suggested that if the broadening of the line for DNA solutions were due to energy exchanges between the nuclear spins of protons of water entering the hydration shell and those of protons of water already in the shell, the hydration of DNA would have to depend upon a special mechanism. Balazs, Bothner-By, and Gergely favored an explanation of the line broadening in terms of diamagnetic anisotropy effects. However, this explanation subsequently has been ruled out (Jardetzky and Brown, 1964). If it were correct, the longitudinal relaxation time of water in DNA solutions should have changed with the square of the stationary magnetic field; instead, it was field-independent. Balazs, et al., suggested that if their results were to be interpreted in terms of hydration shells surrounding the DNA molecules, only rather small shells could be involved, not large domains of ice-like lattice order such as were suggested by Jacobson.*

These studies were followed shortly by those of Douglass, Frisch, and Anderson (1960) whose relaxation-time determinations for tobacco mosaic virus solutions were consistent with the findings of Jardetzky and Jardetzky (1957). However, the explanation advanced by Douglass, et al., for the observed changes, which involved paramagnetic effects and other causes, is inconsistent with the fact that the line broadening can be reversed by dilution in D_2O (Jardetzky and Jardetzky, 1957).

Hechter, Wittstruck, McNiven, and Lester (1960) studied the nuclear magnetic resonance of the water protons in agar gels. The significant broaden-

---

* The reader should note here and in the following that Jacobson specifically qualified the sense in which the lattice order of hydration shells was proposed to be ice-like (see page 34).

41

ing of the line width (from 1.6 ± 0.4 to 16.5 ± 3 cps) and the amplitude decrease which they found for 3% agar gels was not shown by a variety of other gels and viscous solutions (methocel, pectin, carboxymethyl cellulose, etc.). Moreover, the signal of the methyl-group protons from tetramethylammonium chloride was essentially equivalent when studied in agar gels or in pure water, in marked contrast to the water proton signal. Accordingly, these investigators claimed that the changes in the water proton signals in the gel could not be caused by heterogeneity of the internal field resulting from compartmentalization of water, diamagnetic anisotropy, or the presence of paramagnetic impurities. Rather they felt that the NMR data were best explained on the basis of the water in the agar gel being in a modified state.

Hechter, et al. (1960), suggested an interpretation along the lines discussed by Bernal (1959). At the surface of the polysaccharide chains in the agar gel, the water molecules were proposed to be hydrogen-bonded to hydroxyl groups (on a 1:1 or 2:1 basis), this bonding resulting in a rigid "ice-like" arrangement of a small number of the water molecules. The bulk of the water between the polysaccharide chains was suggested to be in a state intermediate between an ice-like arrangement and "free," to the extent that it possessed a certain degree of rigidity (with consequent reduced mobility), while in large part retaining the solvent properties of free water (note the similarities to the degree of ice-likeness proposed by Jacobson; see page 34).

Berendsen (1962) has taken a somewhat different approach to the problem by using broad-line techniques. As mentioned above, Berendsen interpreted his NMR data for collagen solutions in terms of the water molecules forming chains in the fiber direction and of these chains rotating or reorienting about their long axis. According to his analysis, the magnitude and angular dependence of the observed line splitting leave little doubt that the splitting is caused by a dipole-dipole interaction. Berendsen assumed that it was the interaction between the two protons of one water molecule that was responsible.

In another recent NMR study (Depireux and Williams, 1962), it was suggested that the observed broadening of the water-resonance peak for DNA solutions (0.3 to 19%) could be accounted for by "ordinary viscosity effects." However, the changes in line width with concentration were about the same as those found by Odajima, Sohma, and Watanabe (1959) for solutions of fibrous materials. These latter results together with others clearly indicated the relation of the line width to the adsorption processes. Moreover, it is precisely these "ordinary viscosity effects" which the physical chemist is seeking to interpret in terms of structural detail.

In the most recent NMR study of protein hydration (Daszkiewicz, Hennel, Lubas, and Szczepkowski, 1963) it was found that the proton spin-lattice and spin-spin relaxation times were decreased in ovalbumin solutions. This was believed to be caused by an increase of the correlation time (see page 37) of part of the water molecules. According to the calculations of Daskiewicz, et al., water bound rigidly and irrotationally to ovalbumin amounts to only 0.016

gram per gram of dry protein (0.0197 for egg-white). For ovalbumin denatured at 100°C the value increases to 0.123 gram per gram.

Turning to the results of recent NMR line-width and relaxation-time studies of the intracrystalline water in minerals, Pickett and Lemcoe (1959), Sears (1960), and Ducros and Dupont (1962) all concluded that the protons of water in nontronite were very mobile. Studies of water in zeolites (Auerbach, Ducros, and Pare, 1960; Ducros, 1960; Turkevich, Mackay, and Thomas, 1960) showed that here too the water was very mobile at most water contents; whatever restraint there was on the motion of the water was felt to be exerted largely by the cations. Studies of the water in sodium-zeolites by Matyash, Piontovskaya, and Tarasenko (1962) yielded a self-diffusion coefficient of 10^{-7} cm^2 / sec, which is only about one hundredth that for free water. However, all these results must be regarded with caution because of the probable dominant effect of paramagnetic impurities on the line width. The most recent study by Graham, Walker, and West (1964) was on the structure of the water in homo-ionic layer silicates (vermiculite, montmorillonite, and nectorite). These investigators concluded that very slight structure of the water, if any, existed in the osmotic swelling region. In the crystalline swelling region, in which a limited number of individual water sheets exist between the silicate layers, the proton mobility was appreciable but varied with the water content. In a single-crystal study of vermiculite containing two sheets of water between the silicate layers, the water molecules were found to be in hindered rotational movement. However, interpretation was complicated by the anisotropic susceptibility of the crystals and the effects of particle size.

In connection with most of the above studies it should be noted that, because of their great sensitivity, high-resolution NMR spectrometers usually are operated at attenuation levels which keep the intense narrow line within limits. Thus, the heavy line broadening caused by direct interactions with water molecules at primary adsorption sites does not contribute measurably to the narrow signal, so that the observed resonance signal variations come in large degree from the protons in the mobile water. Broad-line techniques, which appear to be very promising for attacking the problem of hydration of minimally hydrated, essentially solid material, may be expected to cast new light on the problems of macromolecular hydration.

Insofar as the cited NMR findings are concerned it can be concluded that the repeatedly observed decrease in the area under the proton signal has been a function of the settings of the instruments and did not represent a real phenomenon. The broadening of the signal, on the other hand, was real, but on the basis of the published literature alone, its interpretation is uncertain. Until a systematic investigation of the problems involved in the line broadening has been completed, judgments based upon this criterion must be deferred (Jardetzky and Jardetzky, 1962b). It remains possible, for example, that the line broadening in the system of Hechter, et al., was due to phase inhomogeneities, reflecting exchange of water between more and less viscous regions and between the surface of air bubbles and bulk water, in which case it would have a bearing on the structure of their particular solution rather than upon the problem of macromolecular hydration in general (Jardetzky, 1963). Berensen (1962) offered no *direct* evidence to show that the line which he observed was, indeed, attributable to water. It could also be attributed to a group of protons on a collagen side-chain which became free to rotate as the fiber was hydrated (Jardetzky, 1963). In this connection it should be noted that although water molecules are bound to all the polar groups of crystalline myoglobin, there is no obvious sign of order in the water between the molecules (Kendrew, 1962).

Recent infrared spectroscopic studies of DNA solutions by Depireux and Williams (1962) did not reveal a shift of the 4.7μ band to shorter wave-lengths at lower temperatures, which the investigators felt would be expected if DNA had the influence on water structure proposed by Jacobson. However, there is no justification for assuming that the infrared spectrum of a DNA solution at room temperature should correspond to the spectrum of pure water at a lower temperature (see Kujumzelis, 1938; Bergqvist and Forslind, 1962; and below). Furthermore, the 4.7μ infrared band (2170 cm^{-1} Raman band) is expected to be rather insensitive to the structural changes produced by coupling the heavy masses of macromolecules to the water lattice (Forslind, 1963). This follows from the fact that the hindered rotation potential minimum is rather broad and shallow, since the 4.7μ band usually is taken to represent a combination frequency of hindered rotation and molecular-symmetric bending. Accordingly, small shifts of the maximum in the broad band hardly would be discernible in the concentration range investigated (Forslind, 1963). Unfortunately, the 4.7μ band is the only band of the water spectrum that is not overlapped by the bands from the DNA molecule.

Thus, most of the infrared and nuclear magnetic resonance studies of water-lattice stabilization in macromolecular solutions that have been performed to date leave much to be desired, both from the experimental and theoretical points of view. Repetition and re-evaluation are necessary before significance can be attached to the results of these approaches.

Studies of density gradient systems at sedimentation equilibrium in the ultracentrifuge (Hearst and Vinograd, 1961) provided support for Jacobson's thesis as applied to DNA. Thus, the minimum thickness of the water shell about the T-4 bacteriophage DNA molecule in a solution of lithium silico-tungstate was estimated to be 11 to 12A, on the assumption of complete exclusion of the salt. This corresponds to approximately four layers of water molecules. If the salt were not excluded completely from the hydration crust, the extent of the salt-poor hydration crust would be even greater (Hearst and Vinograd, 1961).

Recent measurements of the self-diffusion coefficient of water in a viscous suspension of carboxymethyl cellulose by an isotopic method (involving O^{18} enrichment) have given values differing but little from the value in pure water

(Higdon and Robinson, 1962). The same results were obtained by Higdon and Robinson using NMR spin-echo techniques. Recall, in this connection, that Hechter, et al. (1960), found no broadening of the water proton resonance line in viscous suspensions of carboxymethyl cellulose.

Some of the other data and arguments marshalled by Jacobson in support of water-lattice stabilization in DNA solutions also have been subjected to a searching experimental and theoretical analysis. Most telling is the finding that the neglect of charge transport processes arising from the motion of ions and other charge carriers in the bulk solution, in the double layer, and in the solute particles themselves can lead to serious errors in the interpretation of dielectric constant, dielectric dispersion, and conductivity data of solutions of polyelectrolytes (O'Konski, 1960). Unfortunately, the Debye and Falkenhagen (1928), Onsager (1926, 1927), and Fuoss and Onsager (1955, 1957) treatments of the dielectric constant and conductivity of simple electrolyte solutions are not adequate for polyelectrolytes, where particle shape and size are important parameters of the system. The formulation of an adequate theory for poly-electrolytes and colloidal electrolytes requires consideration of the charge transport processes (O'Konski, 1960).

When external fields are applied to electrolyte solutions to study their electrical properties, the double layer of the solute particles becomes polarized (ionic polarization), with the consequent production of a dipole moment. This displacement of the center of the double-layer charge from the center of the fixed-ion charge results in a retarding local field which depresses the equivalent conductivity of an ion below the infinite dilution value—the "relaxation effect." For highly-charged polyelectrolytes one expects this effect to be larger than it is for simple electrolytes (O'Konski, 1960). In addition, excess conductivity arises from the mobility of counterions at the interface and from the charge transport due to counterions in thin double layers. O'Konski (1960) was able to express these excess conductivity effects in terms of a generalized surface conductivity including contributions from all counter-ion species and from other charge carriers, such as protons, electrons, and holes confined to a thin region on or near the interface. The electrical boundary value problem then was formulated in terms of this generalized surface conductivity, of the dielectric constant and volume conductivity of the medium, and of an anisotropic dielectric constant and volume conductivity for the particle, all of which parameters have important physical significance for macromolecular structures.

The resulting model appears to be more acceptable for polyelectrolytes than the Debye-Falkenhagen model, inasmuch as it explains many features related to the size and structure of the particles. At the same time it is more realistic than the Maxwell-Wagner theory of ionic polarization (see Wagner, 1915; Fricke, 1953; O'Konski, 1960), for the latter theory requires internal volume conductances too high to be reasonable for substances with compact structure. Virtually all of the known dielectric properties of aqueous solutions of proteins,

45

nucleic acids, nucleoproteins, and other charged colloids appear to be explicable in terms of the model. In particular it can account for remarkably high dielectric increments, for conductivity increments, and for a broad range of relaxation behavior, all of which previously had been attributed to orientation-polarization effects.

That counterions may exert important effects on the electrical properties of polyelectrolytes has been known for some time (see Havestadt and Frick, 1930, 1931; Errera, Overbeek, and Sack, 1935; Heller, 1942). However, the extent of the counterion influence was not appreciated clearly until recently, when experimental studies of electrical birefringence (the Kerr effect), dielectric dispersion, and anisotropy of conductivity established the important and sometimes dominant role of the counterion polarization.

The very strong electric orientation which persisted at frequencies far above the expected orientational dispersion region of DNA solutions and which was dependent upon electrolyte concentration led O'Konski and Zimm (1950) to suggest a role for the ion atmosphere in this behavior. Later it was suggested that the high dielectric increments of polyelectrolytes probably were associated with counterion migration (Dintzis, Oncley, and Fuoss, 1954). The latter workers also noted that the shape of the dielectric curves for aqueous solutions of poly-4-vinyl-n-butylpyridinium bromide suggested the existence of two dispersion regions. Both of these observations are consistent with O'Konski's (1960) model.

O'Konski and Haltner (1957) subsequently pointed out that, in order to explain the electric orientation of tobacco mosaic virus in terms of Jacobson's model, an unreasonably thick hydration crust would have to be assumed. In the case of hemocyanin, a hydration crust (40 ml ice / ml protein) hundreds of angstroms thick would be required (O'Konski, 1960). Since DNA molecules are known to be highly charged, O'Konski suggested that all of the observed electrical properties of DNA solutions, as well as those of other polyelectrolytes could be explained in terms of double-layer (ionic) polarization without invoking the existence of extensive ice-like hydration crusts (see also O'Konski, 1964).

Recently, Stellwagen, Shirai, and O'Konski (1964) studied the dielectric properties and electric birefringence of aqueous NaDNA solutions. Two dielectric dispersions were found, one below 10^5 cps and one in the range 10^6 to 2×10^7 cps. The fact that the dielectric increment calculated from the theoretical surface conductivity (see O'Konski, 1960) agrees in magnitude with the experimental value strongly suggests that the high-frequency dielectric dispersion arises from ionic polarization (see also Johnson and Neale, 1961). Ionic polarization also is indicated by the decrease in the dielectric increment and the reduction in the critical frequency when lithium counterions (which have lower conductance) are substituted for sodium counterions. The existence of a large-amplitude, low-frequency dielectric dispersion indicates

that the DNA molecules in solution possess large permanent dipole moments.*
Some experiments on proteins also suggest that permanent dipole orientation
effects are important (Squire, Moser, and O'Konski, 1964).

In view of these findings it seems unnecessary to postulate the existence
of ice-like hydration crusts hundreds of angstroms thick to account for the
dielectric properties and conductivity of polyelectrolyte solutions.

In conclusion it can be suggested that the interfaces of biological membranes
(and colloids in general) with aqueous phases are encased in a thin crust of
bound water molecules at least one molecule thick. The weight of the more
conclusive evidence argues against gross (i.e., long-range) *immobilization* of
water into thick *ice-like* hydration crusts about macromolecules. But NMR
and other studies make it clear that *ordering* and *immobilization* do not go
hand in hand. Thus, the *net* time which solvent water molecules spend in a
given orientation doubtless is lengthened to varying degrees in solutions of
macromolecules.† However, the lengthening is only from about 10^{-11} seconds
to 10^{-9} or, at most, 10^{-8} seconds, which falls far short of the time of 10^{-5}
seconds or longer for the water molecules in ice (Jardetzky, 1963). The degree
of polarization, and compression or expansion, of the water lattice in the
hydration crust depends upon the specific binding interactions. Precise determination of the extent of long-range ordering of water near micellar interfaces
and near other interfaces having quasi-crystalline structure that are of
biological significance remain important problems for future studies.

Proton mobility

Mobility of protons in water and ice. The existence of a continuous crust of
bound water at membrane interfaces should have important effects on the
mobility of hydronium and hydroxyl ions; it also should facilitate electron
transfer (see Klotz, 1962).

The majority of the protons in water are expected to be associated with
water molecules and, by their presence, to intensify the temporary hydrogen
bonds between these molecules and their neighbors, giving the proton a large
thermodynamic hydration number (Robinson and Stokes, 1959). Studies of
the dielectric and thermal properties of aqueous solutions, in fact, lead to the
conclusion that the symmetrical molecule-ion, ‡ H_3O^+, is strongly hydrated in
the same way as are other small univalent cations. There is compelling evidence (including mass spectroscopy) for a stable $H_9O_4^+$ complex held together

* Polarization of the counterion atmosphere reduces the internal field and thus diminishes the
permanent dipole polarization (O'Konski, 1960).

† This is not to imply that the time spent in a given orientation by the water molecules near
charged groups on macromolecules is not shortened as a result of the structure-breaking effects
of these groups (see below). Most of the techniques employed measure only the change in the
net time spent in a given orientation.

‡ Hydronium ions in crystals are flat pyramids of symmetry $3m$ (see Richards and Smith,
1951; Yoon and Carpenter, 1959; White and Burns, 1963).

by very strong hydrogen bonds (Wicke, Eigen, and Ackermann, 1954; Bascombe and Bell, 1957; Wyatt, 1957; Beckey, 1958; see also Eigen, 1963), together with a secondary hydration shell of relatively loosely bound water molecules. For simplicity in the following discussion the solvated proton, whether H_3O^+ or $H_9O_4^+$, generally is referred to merely as a hydronium ion. Recently it was suggested that the hydroxyl ion has a similar effect on water structure (Ackermann, 1961).

In ordinary water most ions have mobilities falling in the range 4.0 to 8.3×10^{-4} cm / sec, while the mobility of the slowest ions is at least 2.0×10^{-4} cm / sec. However, the mobilities of hydronium ions (36.2×10^{-4} cm / sec) and hydroxyl ions (19.8×10^{-4} cm / sec) are much greater (see Eigen and De Maeyer, 1958), even though the radius of the hydrated proton (about 4.5A) exceeds that of any other univalent monatomic ion. The enhanced mobility of hydronium and hydroxyl ions generally is believed to depend upon the phenomenon of fast proton transfers between the water molecules and the ions (see Grotthuss, 1806; Hückel, 1928; Bernal and Fowler, 1933; Gierer and Wirtz, 1949; Conway, Bockris, and Linton, 1956). Even at the low concentration of $10^{-6.998}$ M / liter of hydronium and hydroxyl ions in pure water at 25°C, each water molecule is involved in such transfers more than 1,000 times per second (see below). The pressure dependence of proton mobility also is anomalous; in contrast to normal ionic behavior, proton mobility increases with increasing pressure (see Eigen and De Maeyer, 1958). The following discussion is limited primarily to the factors involved in the mobility of hydronium ions and is based largely upon the treatments of Conway, Bockris, and Linton (1956) and Eigen and De Maeyer (1958, 1959).

Conduction of protons in water and in a number of other hydrogen-bonded solvents is completely different from classical ion migration and bears more resemblance to the process of electron transport in semi-conductors. According to inferences based upon quantum-mechanical theory, a hydronium ion in close contact with a suitably oriented water molecule need not retain its extra proton, for there is another possible configuration of equal energy in which the extra proton has transferred between molecules (the proton oscillating very rapidly within the $H_9O_4^+$ complex). Thus, whenever a water molecule is oriented in such a way that one of its $2p_z$ orbitals is in line with an O—H bond of a neighboring hydronium ion, the proton is believed to tunnel rapidly from the hydronium ion to the water molecule. The conductance mechanism over greater distances can be visualized as a chain migration by such quantum-mechanical tunneling through and along the direction of a series of hydrogen bonds (i.e., a structural diffusion of the hydration complex, $H_9O_4^+$), followed by electron-cloud fluctuations (rehybridizations). In each step the excess proton, so to speak, jumps about 0.86A between adjacent water molecules, while the positive charge moves nearly 3.1A.

At least 90% of the protons are believed to be transported by such tunnel transfers although they spend only 1% of their time in the transfer process (which requires less than 10^{-13} seconds). The fact that the proton spends most of the time in association with a definite water molecule (or complex of water molecules) is responsible for the existence of the hydronium ion and is in agreement with the molecular and thermal properties ascribed to the hydronium ion in aqueous solution—infrared spectra, ionic refractivity, partial molal heat content, etc.

The activation energy for proton transfer between hydronium ions and water molecules is less than that for defect proton transfer. In the latter, the potential function becomes steeper because the proton transfers between two residual negative charges. Moreover, the protons in the hydronium ion probably are slightly more peripherally located and slightly less tightly bound than in H_2O, because of the repulsive effects of the extra proton. Accordingly, the hydronium ion has a greater mobility than the hydroxyl ion, in spite of its greater hydration.

The migration of a proton through hydrogen bonds changes the dipole orientations of the water molecules in the chain (see equation 12). Accordingly, thermal reorientation of the hydrogen-bonded water molecules in the field of the proton must occur before further protons can transfer in the same direction through the same hydrogen-bonded chain. In the presence of an external electrostatic field, however, alignment of the hydronium ion (as a result of its dipole moment) more often favors the transfer of a proton in the direction of the field than in other directions, so that proton transfers probably contribute to *electrical conductivity* by a self-regulating mechanism (Hückel, 1928; Bernal and Fowler, 1933).

Rotational rearrangements to provide favorable orientations for proton transfer (preceded and followed by fast tunneling) are believed to be rate-determining in water, whereas the quantum-mechanical tunneling of the proton itself is believed to be rate-determining in ice. Thus, as the proton activity in water is lowered, the number of protons transferring through any given water molecule and the number of rotations of the molecule in the field of the protons is reduced. Eventually, at a point where the proton activity is low enough, the rotational rate of water molecules required to transfer the reduced number of protons flowing in a given direction is less than the spontaneous thermal rotation rate under the same conditions. At this point, the rate of proton transport no longer is controlled by the rotation of water molecules but is controlled by the rate of quantum-mechanical tunneling. Accordingly, the mobility of the protons can increase until it reaches the much greater value allowed by the new rate-determining process.

Since the proton concentration in ice is only about 1 / 1,000 to 1 / 100 of that in water at the same temperature,* and since it is in the range where quantum-mechanical tunnel transfer is rate-determining, enhanced mobility of protons in ice over that in water at the same temperature is qualitatively

* For example, at $-10°C$ the proton concentration in water is 2.8×10^{-8} g ion / liter, while in ice at the same temperature it is only 3 to 15×10^{-11} g ion / liter (Eigen and De Maeyer, 1956).

accounted for. Since water and ice have roughly the same electrical conductivity, the lower proton activity must be compensated by the higher mobility. Proton mobility in ice, in fact, is 10 to 100 times greater than that in water (for example, $1,900 \times 10^{-4}$ cm / sec at $-10°C$), approaching to within a factor of 50 the electron mobility in semi-conductors and some metals. The ice crystal might thus be considered as a "proton semi-conductor."

On the other hand, Forslind (1963) cautions against unreserved acceptance of tunneling* as a working hypothesis to explain proton exchange in aqueous systems. It is by no means fully established that the tunneling mechanism is responsible for the proton transfer in the hydrogen bond, while it is known that the transfer is inhibited as soon as the conjugation characteristics associated with the rehybridization mechanism of the bonded system are prevented. In this connection it is important to note that the tunneling phenomenon does not involve the breaking down or reduction of the potential barrier and that the whole process, when it occurs, proceeds as if the barrier were nonexistent (Forslind, 1963).

Although, in Forslind's view, tunneling cannot be excluded completely as a mechanism for proton jumps, the probability of its occurrence is proposed to be extremely small. It is suggested that the mechanism which is reponsible almost exclusively for proton jumps involves breakdown of the potential barrier and its reconstitution after the jumps, and that these modulations of the barrier depend upon thermally induced rehybridization waves of the oxygen lattice. Forslind contends that only this mechanism of proton jumps is able to account for retention of the individuality of the water molecules in the ice lattice (see also the discussion of ion-water interactions on page 66).

Forslind (1963) also suggests that the concept of a complex between a hydronium ion and water in *dilute* solutions is unnecessary and misleading. According to him the incorporation of hydronium ions into the water lattice violates the condition of retention of the individuality of the water molecules in the lattice. In those cases of experimental verification of the existence of hydronium ions—crystalline systems, such as the solid monohydrates, $H_3O^+NO_3^-$, and $H_3O^+ClO_4^-$ (Richards and Smith, 1951; Wicke, Eigen, and Ackermann, 1954), and highly concentrated complexing solutions—there is no question of the incorporation of an H_3O^+ ion into a water lattice.

Theoretical calculations carried out for the coupling of the hydronium ion into a system of surrounding water molecules (Grahn, 1961, 1962), while they are based upon arbitrary boundary conditions that cannot be satisfied in aqueous solutions, nonetheless have given results of great interest. These results help to clarify the question of whether a stable, free complex of a hydronium ion and water molecules can exist.

Proton exchanges in water and electrolyte solutions have been studied by nuclear magnetic resonance (Gutowsky and Saika, 1953; Hood, Redlich, and Reilly, 1954; Meiboom, Luz, and Gill, 1957; Meiboom, 1961; Luz and Meiboom, 1963a). The proton exchange rate in natural water is both acid and

* For a recent discussion of the proton-tunneling process, see Löwdin (1963).

base catalyzed and is so fast that, except for a small pH range around neutrality, exchange narrowing of the proton resonance lines occurs, i.e., only a single, collapsed, nearly Lorentzian line (with a width of from about 1 to 2.4 cps) is found. Since the addition of acid or base increases the proton exchange rate, narrowing of the resonance width occurs (but other factors also may contribute to the narrowing).

At first it was assumed that the Larmor resonance frequency lines involved in the exchange narrowing corresponded to hydrogen-bonded and "free" protons (Meiboom, Luz, and Gill, 1957). However, the predominant splitting of the proton resonance (i.e., the greatest contribution to the broadening) now is known to be due to a spin-spin interaction with O^{17},* the magnitude of the broadening being roughly proportional to the O^{17} concentration. This fine-structure splitting is only partially averaged out by proton exchange (Meiboom, 1961), and the excess width of the resulting proton line in O^{17}-enriched water over that in non-enriched water provides a measure of the direct proton-exchange rate between water molecules.

Meiboom's (1961) studies of the transverse relaxation rate of the proton resonance and his direct line-width measurements of the exchange broadening of the O^{17} resonance in O^{17}-enriched water† as a function of pH (adjusted with HCl and KOH) are in quantitative agreement and provide a direct determination (to within about 40%) of the rate constants of the excess and defect proton transfer reactions (10.6 and 4.8 $\times$ 10^9 liter / mole-sec, respectively; see also Luz and Meiboom, 1963a). These rates are consistent with those inferred long ago from anomalous conductance results.

Since the structure of much of the hydration crust which covers membrane interfaces probably is modified in the direction of that of ice, it is to be anticipated that the proton mobility along continuous hydrogen-bonded pathways through the crust will exceed that in the adjacent water—the crust facilitating proton transfers. Thus, changes in proton potential resulting from local changes in proton activity should be transmitted preferentially along topologically connected pathways within the crust, somewhat as electrons are transmitted along a wire, rather than decaying through exchanges with the cytoplasmic matrix by isotropic volume conduction. Since changes in interfacial proton activity would affect interfacial potentials, both directly and via their effects on dipole orientations, they could mediate cationic displacements and at the same time have direct influences on lipid head-group orientation.

Mobility of protons relative to binding sites. In addition to a probable in-

* O^{17} has a natural abundance of 0.037% and a spin of $\frac{5}{2}$, whereas the two other stable oxygen isotopes, O^{16} and O^{18} have zero spin. If no exchange were taking place, the proton resonance spectrum would consist of seven lines—a central line due to the protons bonded to O^{16} and O^{18} atoms, and six equally-spaced lines due to the protons bonded to O^{17} atoms.

† In the absence of exchange, the O^{17} resonance would consist of a spin-spin triplet due to spin-spin interaction with two equivalent protons.

creased mobility of protons in the hydration crust of membranes by virtue of enhanced proton transfers, protons which are associated with ionizable groups probably also become more "mobile" in relation to their binding sites; i.e., proton associations become looser. The basis for this phenomenon is that in the physiological pH range, the number of polar groups in membrane interfaces able to bind protons ($>PO_4^-$, —COO$^-$, —NH$_2$, etc.) will exceed the number of protons bound (the charge balance being preserved by other counter-cations). Accordingly, there will exist many possible configurations of associated protons between possible binding sites. Since these configurations differ but little in free energy, thermally induced total charge fluctuations and fluctuations between configurations will occur (Kirkwood and Shumaker, 1952).

In view of these considerations, the interfacial regions of biological membranes probably are highly labile domains with respect to factors influencing proton activity, binding, and mobility. The activity of other ions probably is the most important factor in this regard, and according to the theories of the author, competitive interactions of other cations and protons with anionic binding sites* plays a basic role in membrane transformations. It is important, then, to consider the effects of the hydration crust on the mobility of other cations and whether other cations also would participate in thermally induced charge and charge-distribution fluctuations. With respect to the latter phenomenon, other cations can participate and, accordingly, also would become more "mobile" insofar as binding is concerned (Kirkwood, 1957). Thus the presence of a relatively small number of vacant cationic binding sites increases the dissociation energy of all associated counterions (Ling, 1962). However, the bodily transport rate of other counterions would be reduced because of the high viscosity of the hydration crust (see Davies and Rideal, 1961; Klotz, 1962).

The Effects of Ions on Water Structure. Ions have an effect on water over and above the simple dielectric polarization, binding, and compression of near-neighbor molecules, namely a structure-breaking action, i.e., a shift in the structure-equilibrium in the direction of a smaller degree of ice-likeness (Bernal and Fowler, 1933; Cox and Wolfenden, 1934; Stewart, 1939, 1943, 1944; Frank and Evans, 1945; Eucken, 1948; Gurney, 1953). Moreover, the effects of ionic structure-disturbing centers are not limited to the hydration shell immediately adjacent to the ion.† Through the torque which their electric fields exert on water dipoles, ions both interfere with the initiation of

* Some aspects of the atomic factors determining this competition have been studied by Eisenman (1961, fig. 7; 1962, fig. 15).

† For example, the most rapid change in apparent molal ionic volume with concentration is at the greatest dilution, which indicates that the ions have effects on water molecules beyond their nearest-neighbors (Stewart, 1939).

clusters (i.e., hydrogen-bonding) and hasten cluster disruption* (Frank and Wen, 1957).

Although they cause entropy losses of comparable magnitude to those due to icebergs around non-polar groups, some ions actually lessen the entropy losses relative to those of equivalent non-polar groups (Frank and Evans, 1945; Powell and Latimer, 1951), i.e., they promote increased disorder in the water. For example, the entropy loss on dissolving a potassium and a chloride ion (both of which have the electronic structure of argon) in water is appreciably less than the loss on dissolving two argon atoms. Bernal and Fowler (1933) introduced the concept of a "structural temperature," defined as the temperature at which pure water has the same internal structure and the same viscosity as the water in the solution under consideration. They considered that some ions increase the structural temperature, while other ions decrease it. According to their criterion, the ion-water dipole interaction energy had to exceed the potential energy of a water molecule in liquid water (15,300 cal / mole) in order for a hydrated ion to form.

Among the observed effects of ions in aqueous solutions (relative to pure water) are the production of changes in the intensity of the bands in the infrared and Raman absorption spectra (involving frequency shifts in the scattered radiation), changes in the radial distribution function obtained by X-ray scattering, changes in the magnetic resonance of protons, and changes in the viscosity, density, temperature of maximum density, dielectric constant, and dielectric relaxation time.

According to Frank and co-workers (Frank and Evans, 1945; Frank and Wen, 1957), three concentric regions surround an ion:

1) an innermost structure-forming region of polarized, immobilized, and electrostricted water molecules;

2) an intermediate structure-broken region in which the water is less ice-like, i.e., more random in organization, than ordinary water; and

3) an outer region containing water having the normal liquid structure.

This scheme, which is supported by experimental studies of many properties of aqueous ionic solutions, is adopted as a working hypothesis.

The breaking of the structure of water in the intermediate region about an ion may be considered to be caused by the approximate balance between the two competing, relatively ordered, inner and outer influences which act on the water molecules in this region (see Frank and Evans, 1945; Gurney, 1953; Frank and Wen, 1957; Harris and O'Konski, 1957), i.e., the normal tetrahedral structure-orienting influence of neighboring unperturbed water molecules, versus the radially orienting, polarizing influence of the spherically-symmetrical electric field of the ion.†

---

* In the Forslind (1953) view, ions increase the asymmetry of the intermolecular thermal vibrations and the probability of lattice-defect formation (see also Bergqvist and Forslind, 1962).

† See Figure IV-2 in Gray (1962) for an illustration of an analogous effect.

The ion-water interaction

ANIONS VERSUS CATIONS. The most favorable way to fit an ion into a water cluster would be to have the ion at the center of a tetrahedron, with the four nearest-neighbor water molecules about it having their oxygen atoms at the corners, an arrangement consistent with observed heats of hydration (Bernal and Fowler, 1933; Gurney, 1953; Eisenman, 1961). But even if the tetrahedral configuration were assumed by water molecules in the spherically-symmetrical electric field, and the tetrahedron were of the right size, it still could not fit into a cluster, for all four water molecules would be polarized toward the same center.

In the case of the perchlorate ion, the tetrahedral arrangement of the oxygen atoms around the chlorine atom very closely resembles the water tetrahedron with regard to shape and molecular dimensions (Forslind, 1953). When subjected to fields of the surrounding, coordinated water molecules, the oxygen atoms of the perchlorate ion may form hydrogen bonds to the water without greatly disturbing the structural order of the water lattice. The tetrahedrally structured ammonium ion has only a very small effect on the viscosity of water (and of sulfuric acid). Accordingly, it is believed to have only a very small structure-breaking effect (Frank and Evans, 1945). It seems likely that this ion, with its four protons and its ability to form hydrogen bonds, fits well into the structure of liquid water and sulfuric acid (Frank and Robinson, 1940; Fajans and Johnson, 1942; Gillespie, 1957). In fact, the ammonium ion is unique in its similarity to water. Ammonium ions and water have almost identical masses and partial molar volumes, and very similar bonding angles and interatomic distances. Because of the strong polarity of the O—H bond in water, the "electrostatic" forces exerted on their nearest neighbors by a neutral water molecule and a charged ammonium ion are probably very similar (Vollmer, 1963). In particular, both H_2O and NH_4^+ form hydrogen bonds of about the same strength.

One of the main problems in the field of ion-water interactions is to account for the differences between the interaction of water molecules with anions as opposed to the interaction with cations. As a result of these differences the absolute free energies and enthalpies of hydration of anions generally are believed to be somewhat greater than those for cations of the same size and magnitude of charge,* while the absolute entropies of hydration are believed to be very much greater than for comparable cations (Latimer, Pitzer, and Slansky, 1939; Noyes, 1962). To take an extreme example, the calculated enthalpy of hydration of F^- is 47,000 cal / mole greater than that of K^+ (Buckingham, 1957).

Around a cation, the configuration of minimum energy is one in which the two O—H bonds point outward while the two centers of negative charge (on the oxygen atom) are oriented toward the ion, forming a linkage which

* The uncertainty concerning whether the hydration energies of anions are greater than those of cations revolves around the question of the validity of the Born model for ion-water interact ons (see below).

is essentially different in character from the hydrogen bond. The cation and the oxygen and hydrogen atoms are coplanar. This arrangement presumably does not permit rotation of the water molecule (so-called "irrotational binding"), except possibly around the dipole axis—a motion that does not contribute to the orientation polarization. Apparently cations having a wide range of sizes lead to configurations that adapt themselves well to the surrounding water structure (Noyes, 1962). Since a water molecule interacts with a cation through both lone pairs of L-shell electrons, it can bond to a total of only two other water molecules.

Around anions (which generally are supposed to be considerably less hydrated than cations) the protons in the water molecule, being centers of positive charge, tend to be directed toward the ion. In this situation, the possible configurations of the nearest-neighbor water molecules apparently are more sharply dependent on the size of the central ion than they are for cations (see Noyes, 1962). It has been suggested that the water molecules tend to orient with one of their O—H bonds normal to the ion surface, the interaction between the anion and the water being similar to a hydrogen bond* (see treatments of ion-water interactions by Bernal and Fowler, 1933; Eley and Evans, 1938; Coulson and Everett, 1940; Verwey, 1942; Stokes and Robinson, 1948; Moelwyn-Hughes, 1948; Haggis, Hasted, and Buchanan, 1952; Harris and O'Konski, 1957; Waldron, 1957; Brady, 1958, 1960; Syrnikov, 1958; Hindman, 1962). This would leave the anion-bound water molecule freer to rotate than a cation-bound water molecule (with a contribution to the orientation polarization), and would permit it to form hydrogen bonds to three other water molecules. Dielectric constant determinations tend to support this general conception of differences in the method of binding of water by anions and cations (Hasted, Ritson, and Collie, 1948; Haggis, Hasted, and Buchanan, 1952; Harris and O'Konski, 1957).

Small anions and cations that oppositely polarize their nearest-neighbor water molecules may, then, ion-pair through the intermediary of one or more polarized water molecules. This is the process of "localized hydrolysis" postulated by Robinson and Harned (1941) to explain the reversed order of the activity and osmotic coefficients of the alkali hydroxides, acetates, and probably of the fluorides; a postulate which was extended by Diamond (1958) to explain the reversal in order of the coefficients of the smaller alkali-metal and alkaline-earth halide salts from the normal halide order observed with the larger cations. For another view of the influence of the water-structure-altering properties of ions on ion-pair formation, see Kessler, Povarov, and Gorbanev (1962).

Buckingham (1957) analyzed the ion-water interaction in terms of a model in which the nearest-neighbors of the ions are bound rigidly in either the

---

* Recall, in this connection, that in the clathrates of peralkylated salts, the anions are believed to be a hydrogen-bonded part of the host lattice (Beurskens-Kerssen, Jeffrey, and McMullan, 1963).

tetrahedral or octahedral configuration, and the solvent beyond the primary hydration shell is represented by a continuum having the bulk properties of pure water (as assumed in the development of the Kirkwood theory of dielectric polarization of polar liquids). His findings led him to question the assumption that the most favorable orientation for a water molecule next to an anion finds one of the protons on a line joining the center of the ion to the oxygen atom. He pointed out that in this configuration the dipole of the water molecule is at an angle of 52° to the electric line of force, whereas the minimum dipolar interaction energy is for an angle of 0°. Buckingham (1957) suggested, in fact, that an angle of 0° was compatible with the available data.

Buckingham's analysis of the ion-water interaction showed that the energy of the ion-quadrupole interaction is of significant magnitude,* and he suggested that this interaction was the chief cause for the difference between the heats of hydration of comparable anions and cations. Thus, on changing the sign of the ionic charge (keeping the radius fixed) the water dipole must be inverted to retain the large ion-dipole energy. But if the ion-dipole energy remains unchanged, the sign of the ion-quadrupole term is reversed (the sign of the dipole-quadrupole interaction term—between the water molecules— also changes on inversion). Since the magnitude of the ion-quadrupole interaction energy (for K^+ and F^-) is 39% of that for the ion-dipole interaction, the total contribution to the interaction energy due to these two components differs by a factor of as much as 2.28, according to the sign of the charge.

Buckingham's approach has been extended by Vaslow (1963). Vaslow assumed with Buckingham that both the polarization interaction (due to the polarizability of the adjacent water molecule) and the interaction of the ion with bulk water outside the cavity were isotropic. He evaluated only anisotropic contributions to the interaction energy and assumed that the dipole and quadrupole terms were the only terms giving large anisotropic contributions. Accepting the quadrupole moment estimated by Buckingham, and the rigorous potential energy equation, Vaslow showed that the position of minimum potential energy for small cations does not lie on the dipole axis of the water molecule, but at a substantial angle to that axis. Upon the basis of this finding, he suggests that two or more water molecules adjacent to the same small cation might have an orientation that would allow their mutual hydrogen bonding (with some bending of the bond). In that event, hydration of small cations could be consistent with the normal hydrogen-bonded structural groupings in liquid water (Vaslow, 1963).

Another difference between the anion and cation interactions with water could depend upon the center of positive charge of the water-molecule dipole being closer to the surface of the molecule than the center of negative charge. Thus, the permanent dipole could come closer to anions than to comparable

---

* Buckingham's numerical results are, however, open to some doubt, for he arbitrarily equated a Born-model heat of hydration difference, between positive and negative ions of the same radius, to a quadrupole term (see Everett, 1957).

cations, leading to larger ion-dipole energies for anions (Latimer, Pitzer, and Slansky, 1939; Buckingham, 1957; Noyes, 1962). However, this factor probably would not play a major role in determining the differences in thermodynamic properties in cation versus anion hydration.

The distortion of the electron charge-cloud of water molecules (distortion polarization) would be much the same in the neighborhood of both types of ions—namely, fewer electrons on the average would be found in the neighborhood of the protons. Thus, near cations, the water molecules on the average would have their charge-cloud density increased in the neighborhood of the apposed oxygen atom. Protons would be attracted to anions, and the electrons repelled, also leading to an increased charge-cloud density in the neighborhood of the oxygen atom (Shoolery and Alder, 1955).

The matter of the existence of an appreciable difference in the interactions of solvent water molecules with cations and anions is not settled entirely, even in terms of purely electrostatic models. Mukerjee (1961) assumed that the ion-solvent interaction was such that the partial molal volume of an ion (at infinite dilution) was the algebraic sum of the intrinsic volume of the ion in solution and the volume of electrostriction* of the water (see also Padova, 1963)—with the electrostriction inversely proportional to the radius. Working from this assumption (in terms of Born's continuum model for the solvent) he argued that for spherically symmetrical, large monovalent ions, such as the alkali-metal cations and the halide anions, the partial molal volumes should be a smooth monotonic function of the crystallographic radius,† quite independently of the sign of the charge. Benson and Copeland (1963) have shown that the empirical correlation provided by this hypothesis is quantitatively justifiable by means of the Born electrostatic model for ion solvation (Born, 1920) in terms of an isomorphic replacement of water molecules in a simple cubic lattice by ions whose sizes range from smaller to not too much larger than water.

The usual Born theory of the solvation of an ion by a dielectric medium assumes that both the ion and the medium are incompressible. However, it has been realized for some time that ions are not incompressible and that, owing to the distortions of the electron orbitals in the crystals and the medium-dependent equilibrium between repulsive and attractive forces, their intrinsic radii in solution generally are greater than the crystallographic radii and less than the gaseous radii (see Conture and Laidler, 1957; Hepler, 1957; Laidler and Pegis, 1957; Laidler, 1959; Padova, 1963, 1964; Whalley, 1963).

NET STRUCTURE-MAKING VERSUS NET STRUCTURE-BREAKING. Relatively small ions and multivalent ions, such as Li^+, Na^+, H_3O^+, Ca^{2+}, Ba^{2+}, Mg^{2+}, Al^{3+},

* According to a recent analysis by Whalley (1963), for ions with high dipole and quadrupole moments the compression of the ion appears to be a good deal greater than the electrostriction of the water, provided that dielectric saturation does not occur.

† The model breaks down for the small lithium ion and for polyvalent ions, for which the electrostrictions become independent of the radius.

Er³⁺, HO⁻, and F⁻ increase the viscosity of water and, thus, are said to have net structure-making effects. Their high electric fields not only polarize, immobilize, and electrostrict nearest-neighbor water molecules (i.e., "primary hydration" or the "short-range hydration" of Samoilov, 1957b, 1962), but they induce additional order (entropy loss) beyond the first water layer* (i.e., the "secondary hydration" of Bockris, 1949, and "long-range hydration" of Samoilov, 1957b), encroaching, so to speak, on the structure-broken region. The activation energy for the exchange of nearest-neighbor water molecules about such ions is positive (Samoilov, 1957a), i.e., the primary hydration water is less mobile than bulk water (termed "positive hydration"). According to Samoilov (1957b), primary or short-range hydration should be regarded as the action of ions on the thermal, particularly on the translational, movements of nearest-neighbor water molecules (see also Mikhailov and Syrnikov, 1960).

Although the tetrabutylammonium ion is neither small nor multivalent, it is a strong structure-maker (Frank, 1963a) because of the additional influence of the butyl groups on the water structure. In fact, net structure-making effects should occur with any amphiphile ion large enough to be thought of as a molecule with a charge embedded in it, such as all the tetra-alkyl-ammonium ions (Diamond, 1963). Similarly, the acetate ion is a strong structure-maker, and one also expects the formate ion to be structure-making (Gurney, 1953).

That net structure-making cations exert a predominantly hydrating influence, together with some structure-breaking, tended to be confirmed by early studies of infrared absorption spectra (Suhrmann and Breyer, 1933), the concentration-dependence of the dielectric constant of aqueous solutions (Haggis, Hasted, and Buchanan, 1952), entropies of hydration (Frank and Evans, 1945), apparent molal heat capacities (Eigen and Wicke, 1951), apparent molal volumes (Eucken, 1948), equivalent conductances (Darmois, 1946; Sutra, 1946), and the temperature-dependence of the limiting diffusion coefficient (Wang, 1954b). That ions with particularly high field intensities order water beyond their nearest neighbors was supported by early studies of infrared spectra (Suhrmann and Breyer, 1933), entropies of ionic hydration (Asmus, 1949), apparent molal heat capacities (Eigen and Wicke, 1951), and Ulich's F-values (Ulich, 1936; Asmus, 1949). Some results of the most recent studies are considered in the following discussions.

Er³⁺ presents an unusual example of a net structure-making cation in which there is a firmly held octahedral arrangement of water molecules around the ion. Peaks in the radial distribution curves for solutions of $ErCl_3$ and ErI_3 occur precisely at the distances of the ice spacings but are not present in the curves for pure water (Brady, 1960). Similar findings for Eu³⁺ salts in solution led Freed (1942) to conclude that there was an oriented region of considerable

---

* Feates and Ives (1956) would define the secondary hydration shell as that containing all water molecules which, without substantial loss of translational freedom, experience an order-producing effect exerted by the electrical field of the ion.

extent around the Eu^{3+} ion, while Miller (1958) postulated an ice III structure for the soft ice, with the Eu^{3+} ion fitting interstitially into the lattice. According to Brady (1960), the findings for the Er^{3+} salts provide direct evidence for an ice-like quasi-lattice about the cations in their solutions (Brady, 1960). On the other hand, it has been suggested that these findings are indicative of the formation of a new species that is stable enough to occur as a molecule ion even in the crystalline state (Forslind, 1963).

Large monovalent ions generally have a net structure-breaking (entropy increasing) effect. Because of the dipole-dipole repulsions between solvation-shell molecules, the relatively weak electrostatic field about such ions can cause polarization, immobilization, and electrostriction of water molecules only in the first layer. Beyond this layer a strong structure-breaking effect persists. Thus, ions such as K^+, NH_4^+, Rb^+, Cs^+, Cl^-, Br^-, I^-, NO_3^-, BrO_3^-, IO_3^-, and ClO_4^-, actually increase the fluidity of water.* Non-nearest-neighbor water molecules in the vicinity of these ions probably become more mobile than those in pure water. Hydrogen-bonding groups like $—NH_2$ and $—OH$ may have only a small *net* effect on water structure, since they should be able to enter clusters with only slight distortion and to transmit both cluster-forming and cluster-disrupting tendencies (see Hasted, Ritson, and Collie, 1948; Frank and Wen, 1957; D'Orazio and Wood, 1963).

The view that for most anions and for large monovalent cations the structure-breaking effect predominates over that of ordering nearest-neighbors tended to be confirmed by early investigations of infrared spectra (Suhrmann and Breyer, 1933), apparent partial molar heat capacities (Eigen and Wicke, 1951), changes in the entropy of ionic hydration and the entropy of structure-breaking (Frank and Robinson, 1940; Frank and Evans, 1945), ionic mobilities (Gurney, 1953), the reduction in the time of relaxation of the dielectric constant (Haggis, Hasted, and Buchanan, 1952), and the changes in the self-diffusion coefficient of water in electrolyte solutions (Wang, 1954b).

As the temperature of water is increased, the average cluster size and the number of hydrogen bonds decrease and, accordingly, the net structure-breaking influence of ions like Cl^-, Br^-, and I^- decreases. The viscosity changes due to the effects of the ions thus diminish in importance relative to those caused solely by the rise in temperature (Kaminsky, 1957). It is possible that net structure-making ions increase the viscosity more strongly at higher temperatures, when the concentration of non-hydrogen-bonded water molecules is greater, so that the conditions for binding of water molecules to the ion may be more favorable (Hasted, Ritson, and Collie, 1948; Kaminsky,

---

* Potassium ions generally have been assumed to have a slight net structure-breaking effect. The structure-breaking effect of the perchlorate ion depends upon its entropy of dilution. The weakly structure-altering ammonium ions fit so well into the water lattice that the Raman spectrum of ammonium nitrate solutions remains ostensibly unchanged as the concentration is increased (Vollmer, 1963). On the other hand, when the water molecules surrounding the nitrate ions in dilute solutions are replaced partially by metallic cations, appreciable spectral changes occur.

1957). On the other hand, the effect of long-range ordering of water, which is important for strongly hydrated ions (e.g., Be^{2+}, Mg^{2+}, Li^{2+}), diminishes at higher temperatures because of increased thermal agitation.* Consequently, this viscosity-increasing contribution diminishes (Kaminsky, 1957).

On the other hand, an increase in water fluidity may not necessarily, or even typically, be associated with a structure-breaking effect of the dissolved ion. Thus, NMR results in Forslind's laboratory (Bergqvist and Forslind, 1962; Forslind, 1963) have led to the conclusion that the potassium ion is structure-making, not structure-breaking, i.e., that it increases the binding energy of hydrogen bonds. They also showed that it has density-reducing effects similar to those of dissolved noble-gas atoms (see page 63). The implication of this finding (in terms of the vacant-lattice-point model) is that the dissolved potassium ion replaces an interstitial water molecule that might otherwise have been produced by steric distortion effects (of the potassium ion or the anion) (Forslind, 1963). Thus, since the large potassium ions take over the production of some of the lattice-vibration-attenuation effects otherwise produced by interstitial water molecules, their presence leads to a reduction in the number of interstitial water molecules needed to attain thermal equilibrium in the disturbed lattice. It is proposed that the combination of the lattice-stabilizing effect (i.e., an effect leading to increased hydrogen-bonding) and the prevention of density increase due to lattice disturbance always gives rise to an increased fluidity of the system (Forslind, 1963). This results because the fluidity of the system is very sensitive to the system density—more so than to changes in hydrogen-bond energy. In this view, then, the increase in water fluidity produced by potassium ions is due to the predominance of the effects on density over those on hydrogen-bond energy.

Although the Frank-Wen scheme is adopted as a working hypothesis, it is by no means certain that monovalent ions of large radius can form a complete hydration shell,† or, for that matter, that they can immobilize and electrostrict any water molecules. For certain ions it has been suggested that, in spite of large hydration energies, the nearest-neighbor water molecules are more mobile than in pure water (Samoilov, 1955, 1957a; Krestov, 1962). This is indicated by the finding of negative activation energies of exchange between nearest-neighbor water molecules for large ions, such as K^+, Rb^+, Cs^+, Cl^-, Br^-, and I^-. For the interaction of such ions with water the term "negative hydration" has been employed. In the view of Gurney (1953), there is a critical radius above which the electric field of the ion is too weak to produce

* The first hydration sphere about these ions is largely temperature-independent over the range (12 to 42.5°C) investigated (Darmois, 1946; Sutra, 1946).

† To establish a criterion for saturation of the orientation of a water molecule, i.e., for the removal of a water dipole from the water structure in the vacuum field of the ion and the coupling of the dipole to the ion, Harris and O'Konski (1957) suggested that the ion-dipole coupling energy between the ion and the water molecule should be compared to the energy of breaking a hydrogen bond in water. Unless the former energy is large compared to the latter, saturation of the orientation (attainment of the ion-dipole interaction limit) will not be complete (but see the discussion below on the limitations of electrostatic models).

order in the water. The calculations of Bernal and Fowler (1933; see also Eley and Evans, 1938) indicated that this critical radius would be about 1.6A for monovalent ions (see also below). Accordingly, the electric fields of net structure-breaking ions merely may lower the energy of the water molecules in the water structure in their vicinity to the point where the structure is more susceptible to, and broken up by, thermal agitation.

A similar view regarding the effect of the electric field of an ion (beyond the first coordination sphere) has been taken by Mikhailov and Syrnikov (1960). According to their two-structure water model, the field leads to a displacement of the thermal equilibrium between clusters and closely-packed molecules toward this latter condition. The closely packed molecules in their model correspond to the condition proposed by Samoilov (1946, 1957b), in which interstitial molecules are present and are free to undergo translational displacements through the lattice interstitial cavities.

NUCLEAR MAGNETIC RESONANCE STUDIES. Hindman (1962) has evaluated his nuclear magnetic resonance findings in aqueous solutions of mono-monovalent electrolytes in terms of the view discussed above, namely, that thermally disoriented water can exist in the immediate vicinity of an ion. In his analysis, the effects of ions on the proton magnetic shielding by the electrons in the water molecule are divided as follows:

1) A high-field shift due to the breaking of hydrogen bonds (0.045 ppm per mole of hydrogen bonds broken) in the process of reorienting of the water molecules by the ion, related to the formation of the primary hydration layer.
2) A high-field shift due to the breaking of additional bonds beyond the primary hydration layer, i.e., in the structure-broken region.*
3) A low-field shift due to the distorting effect of the electrostatic field of the ion on the charge-clouds of water molecules—primarily the charge-clouds of nearest-neighbors.
4) A possible additional low-field shift attributable to a change in the electron density around the protons induced by a non-electrostatic interaction between a cation and the oxygen atoms of primary-hydration-shell water.

For cations, Hindman found primary hydration numbers similar to those estimated from other sources, but his results were incompatible with the concept of a *complete* hydration shell of at least four tightly bound water molecules (see also Padova, 1963). The hydration numbers decreased with increasing radius of the cation, and there was an approximately linear relationship between the entropy of hydration of the alkali-metal ions and the "effective" hydration numbers (see also Glueckhauf, 1955). For lithium ions he found evidence for the formation of a complete first hydration shell of four

* If the ion were capable of inducing more hydrogen-bonding in the solution than exists in normal water, a low-field shift would occur.

61

water molecules with additional orientation of water in outer shells (even beyond complete orientation of a second hydration shell).

For anions, however, working from the data for the halide ions, he found that only the fluoride ion forms a hydrate in the chemical sense. The larger halide ions (critical crystallographic radius of 1.7A) act primarily to break down the water structure in their immediate vicinity,* i.e., they undergo negative hydration.

This view of Hindman's, that an anion has a lower interaction energy with a water molecule than does a cation of the same radius, is contrary to the concepts developed by most workers from purely electrostatic models. In some ways, though, it is consistent with certain recent treatments of water-molecule structure (Lennard-Jones and Pople, 1951; Duncan and Pople, 1953; Burnelle and Coulson, 1957). According to these treatments, the largest contribution to the effective dipole moment arises from a high density "ridge" of negative charge associated with the electrons in the lone-pair regions, the contribution from the protons being screened out by the bonding electrons.

The analysis of nuclear magnetic resonance studies of the effects of ions on water structure by Bergqvist and Forslind (1962) also leads to conclusions at variance with the Frank-Wen model. According to Bergqvist and Forslind, the coupling between a simple solute ion and water does not, as a rule, give rise to the formation of a distinct, immobilized coordination sphere of water molecules surrounding the ion, disrupted from the remainder of the lattice, and moving as an entity in the solvent. The dissolved ion is regarded, instead, as integrated into the water lattice by ordinary chemical bonds of variable duration and strength, depending upon the type of instantaneous coupling and the thermal excitation of the lattice (see also below). The dissolved ion is subjected to diffusional translations similar to those occurring in the undisturbed water lattice, which Bergqvist and Forslind believe to take place by the generation and annihilation of lattice defects. In their view, what generally is regarded as exchange with bulk water, is only a shift of position of the dissolved ion in the water lattice, implying a change of neighbors in a series of steps that do not differ in principle from those occurring in ordinary solid diffusion.

It is only in those cases in which dissociated ions tend to form a new molecular species in aqueous medium, involving the incorporation of water molecules into a new stable configuration, that they feel one can speak properly of water immobilization (Forslind, 1963). In the case discussed in the above paragraph, the simple ion retains its individuality as it moves through the water lattice; in the case in which the dissociated ion tends to form a new

---

* The thermodynamic analysis of Padova (1963) agrees in this respect. He proposes that for small monovalent ions, dielectric saturation occurs and one may speak of a hydration shell if the intrinsic radius in solution is less than 1.80A; but if this radius is greater than 1.80A (Rb$^+$, Cs$^+$, Cl$^-$, Br$^-$, I$^-$) only structure-breaking occurs.

molecular species, the complex moves through the lattice in a quite similar way but is subjected to exchange processes in a manner common to all molecular species. In this view, a clear distinction is drawn between water in bulk and water in hydrated solutes, with the configurations of the water in the hydrated solutes having little or nothing to do with the structural properties of bulk water (Forslind, 1963).

Bergqvist and Forslind (1962) find that the calculated ionic molal proton resonance shifts for Cl^-, Br^- and I^- are determined essentially by steric effects. For Na^+ and K^+, steric and distortion polarization effects almost cancel, and both ions are regarded as structure-making (see also above). The shifts calculated for Rb^+ and Cs^+ also indicate a *stabilizing* effect on the water lattice, but they are far from the extreme values for Li^+. The value of the shift for F^- is markedly lower than the values for the other halides.

Recent findings in Forslind's laboratory are pertinent to the comparison of the entropy losses caused by dissolution of potassium chloride as opposed to argon (see page 53). In the case of potassium chloride, chemical bonding between the water lattice and the dissolved ions is believed to occur, whereas in the case of argon atoms the effect on water structure has an almost purely geometric origin. Although two distinct interaction mechanisms are represented by the two cases, both give rise to a *net* decrease in the strength of hydrogen bonds. Thus, the structure-breaking effect of the chloride ions is counterbalanced only partially by the hydrogen-bond stabilizing effect of the potassium ions. Both the potassium and the chloride ions reduce the amplitudes of thermal lattice vibrations and counteract the tendency to increase the density by lattice distortion (see also page 60) (Forslind, 1963). As a result, lattice (dislocation) glide processes are facilitated and the relative viscosity of the system is lowered.

The argon atom, being of slightly greater size than the potassium ion, produces a slight expansion of the interstitial spaces, distorting the lattice and weakening the hydrogen-bonding. Its essential effect, however, is to attenuate the thermal lattice vibration amplitudes in a manner quite similar to the effect of both cations and anions in the case of potassium chloride. The density increase which would have been produced by the steric distortion effects consequently is counteracted, leading to a net reduction of the amplitudes of thermal lattice vibrations and a significant decrease of the entropy of the system (Forslind, 1963). Increases in the fluidity of water caused by potassium and chloride ions thus are believed to depend primarily upon the effects of the ions on solution density, which predominate in the determination of rheological properties (see also page 60).

X-RAY SCATTERING STUDIES. Although nuclear magnetic resonance measurements have the potential to yield significant information about structural changes and ionic processes in electrolyte solutions, the interpretation of NMR findings is far from being well established, for several reasons. For example, the bulk diamagnetic susceptibilities* of the salt solutions often are larger than the proton resonance shifts. This places a serious limitation on the accuracy of results, for the experimental values for the volume (or molal) susceptibilities vary widely and are known accurately for only very few compounds (see Fabricand and Goldberg, 1961; Jardetzky and Jardetzky, 1962b; Kresge, 1963).

Accordingly, the recent findings of Brady and Krause (1957) and Brady (1958), based upon another technique, are highly instructive, but it must be kept in mind that, since they were obtained in concentrated solutions, they may have but limited applicability to dilute solutions. The radial distribution function for pure liquid water obtained by X-ray scattering shows two peaks, one at 2.92A and one at 4.75A, corresponding to the separations of nearest and next-nearest neighbors. When KOH is added to water, there is no shift in these two peaks; they merely become more pronounced. This suggests that the dissolution of KOH is a substitutional process. The potassium ions, which appear to have a hydration number of four, replace water molecules in the quasi-tetrahedral water lattice, contributing to the area of the peaks, which persist even in highly concentrated solutions. The random nature of the liquid state apparently allows relatively minor perturbations in structure without complete breakdown as long as the sizes of the ions going into solution do not differ appreciably from that of a water molecule (crystallographic radius of K^+ and $HO^- = 1.33A$).† Since the potassium ion generally has been thought to have a small net structure-breaking effect, it would appear, upon the basis of the Frank-Wen model, that the structure loss in the intermediate region around potassium ions slightly exceeds the structure gain in the inner region of polarized, immobilized, and electrostricted molecules.

While the results of Brady and Krause (1957) and Brady (1958) indicate a hydration number of four or six for the HO^- ion (see also Glueckhauf, 1955; Ackermann, 1957, 1961), Busig and Hornig (1961) interpret the Raman spectra of KOH solutions to indicate that an HO^- ion is not strongly hydrogen-bonded via its proton but that the ion does interact with at least one water molecule in a strong hydrogen bond.

The lithium ion also appears to have a hydration number of four, but its

---

* Except when one compares the shielding of two or more compounds dissolved in the same solvent, whenever shifts with respect to an external standard are being compared, one must correct explicitly for the difference in the bulk shielding of the sample and reference. This correction is determined by the shape of the sample and the difference in the diamagnetic susceptibilities of the sample and the reference, respectively, and is therefore known as the bulk diamagnetic susceptibility correction (Jardetzky and Jardetzky, 1962b).

† According to the quantitative semi-empirical analysis of Mukerjee (1961), the intrinsic radii of ions in aqueous solution are about 21% greater (78% greater volume) than in the crystal. The earlier, similar analysis of Laidler and Pegis (1957) and Laidler (1959) gave a fair fit of the Born model to free energies and entropies of hydration by expanding the crystallographic radii by about 25%. Hence, an ion with a crystallographic radius of 1.33A would have an intrinsic radius in solution of about 1.61A, close to the average van der Waals radius of the water molecule (about 1.55A). According to the recent calculations of Padova (1963), the intrinsic radius of K^+ in solution is 1.64A.

crystallographic radius is only about one half that of the potassium ion. At a mole fraction of 0.11 of LiCl there is an almost complete absence of the water-water nearest-neighbor peak of 2.92A in the radial distribution function of the solution. Apparently, at this concentration of LiCl, the quasi-tetrahedral water structure is broken down virtually completely. There is every reason to believe that the breakdown of the water structure is brought about chiefly by the lithium ion although, of course, the large size of the chloride ion and the necessity of forcing it into the water structure also must play important roles in determining the final configuration of the solution (Brady, 1958). Since at this mole fraction of LiCl there is virtually no outer region of normal liquid structure remaining, upon the basis of the Frank-Wen model there would be no intermediate structure-broken region either, i.e., in the sense of a more random organization than in ordinary water (since there no longer would be competing, relatively ordered, inner and outer influences). The strong net structure-making influence of lithium ions then manifests itself in an almost complete rebuilding of structure,* in which the hydrated lithium ions pack around the large chloride ions (which are unable to penetrate the hydration shell of the lithium ions), giving the chloride ions an *apparent* hydration number of eight or nine.

INFRARED SPECTROSCOPIC STUDIES. Early workers interpreted changes in the infrared spectrum of water in ionic solutions in terms of changes in the degree of polymerization of the associated liquid (Suhrmann and Breyer, 1933). Subsequent workers interpreted these changes in terms of the "structural temperature" concept introduced by Bernal and Fowler (1933). Thus, it was concluded that large ions generally had effects similar to those produced by increasing the water temperature (i.e., net structure-breaking), whereas small ions, notably F⁻, had the reverse effect (Williams and Gautier, 1939; Williams and Millet, 1944). Kujumzelis (1938), however, studying the Raman spectra of electrolyte solutions, was able to show that the effects produced by dissolved ions are entirely different from those produced by temperature increase. This finding is in accord with most recent concepts (see above) of ion-water interactions. Thus, Bergqvist and Forslind (1962) state that the hydrogen-bond rupture which results from a rise of temperature bears very little resemblance to water-lattice deformations caused by dissolved ions.

Choppin and Buijs (1963) recently studied the same three near-infrared absorption bands of ionic solutions that they had employed for the study of pure water (see page 13). Twelve to one mole-ratio solutions generally had to be used to obtain useful line intensity changes. At this high concentration the zones of influence of the ions must overlap considerably and there must be a considerable degree of ion-pair formation for some solutes. In some cases, such as in solutions of the strong mineral acids and of hydroxides, they were

---

* There will, of course, no longer be any question of water structure, but only a question of aggregates into which water molecules are incorporated. This theme has been elaborated extensively by Mishchenko and co-workers (see Mishchenko and Dymarchuk, 1962).

able to estimate the effect of the solute on the average size of water clusters from changes in line intensities (by computing the mole fractions of water molecules in which zero, one, and both —OH bonds participate in hydrogen-bonding). By comparing these cluster sizes with those for water at the same temperature Choppin and Buijs arrived at the following structure-making and structure-breaking sequences: structure-making cations, $La^{3+} > Mg^{2+} > H_3O^+ > Ca^{2+}$; structure-making anions, $HO^- > F^-$; structure-breaking cations, $K^+ > Na^+ > Li^+ > Cs^+ = Ag^+$; structure-breaking anions, $ClO_4^- > I^- > Br^- > NO_3^- > Cl^- > SCN^-$.

It should be kept in mind that (1) these assignments and sequences hold only in concentrated solutions at 12:1 mole ratios, where ion-pairing and other overlap effects are to be expected; and (2) the quantitative results of Choppin and Buijs depend critically upon the correct assessment of the frequency shifts due to the various degrees of association in the condensed phase. This is a problem which, at the present state of the molecular theory of liquids, involves a good deal of conjecture. Even so, the chief differences from accepted assignments for dilute solutions (see above) are in the strong structure-breaking assignment of K^+, and in the structure-breaking assignments of Na^+ and Li^+ (rather than structure-making). The sequences show interesting correlations with the relative molar shifts of the proton resonance of water assigned by Shoolery and Alder (1955) for concentrated aqueous solutions. In less concentrated solutions Choppin and Buijs found evidence of the expected influence of these ions on water structure. These investigators were careful to point out that ions like Li^+ and Mg^{2+} produce an order which is not identical to the "ice structure" of pure water, whereas H_3O^+ and HO^- presumably can be incorporated directly into clusters.

Shortcomings of electrostatic models and recent alternative considerations. Most of the studies and conclusions cited above on ion-water interactions were based upon purely electrostatic models—either the Born model, the point-charge dipole model, or hybrids of the two. In order to retain a proper perspective, the uncertainties and assumptions of these models should be kept in mind, and attention should be called to recent suggestions of the greater promise of covalent approaches.

The following observations concerning the limitations of electrostatic approaches are those of Magnusson (1964). The uncertainties regarding the interactions of water with cations and anions arise primarily because no experimental measurement of the hydration energies of a single ion exists (see Guggenheim, 1929, 1930; Frank, 1963b). Only the sums of the enthalpies and free energies released in forming electrostatically neutral solutions are known. The Born model attempts to reproduce the experimental energetics of submerging the real gaseous ions in water by calculating, for the cation and anion separately, the sum of the classical electrostatic energies for discharging a conducting sphere in a vacuum, submerging the neutral sphere in water, and recharging it in the dielectric medium. The important adjustable parameters in the model are the radius of the sphere and the dielectric permittivity,* the latter being also a function of temperature, charge, and distance from the sphere.

The point-charge dipole model differs from the pure Born model only in the feature that some or all of the charging energy of the continuous dielectric is replaced by discrete, point-charge dipole interactions. Either model may be elaborated by including saturation of the dielectric, i.e., reduction of the permittivity. The wide acceptance of electrostatic models as reasonable approximations to the real physical processes probably has resulted because of the success with which even the simplest formulations of the theory yield order-of-magnitude agreement with experiment.

Since a considerable body of literature and theory on phenomena in aqueous solutions is being erected on the base provided by the Born model, it is appropriate to review the features of the Born model and to compare them with reality. An important clue to the cation-water interaction is found in the energetics for the formation of solutions of highly charged cations. Consider, for example, the experimentally derived free energy data for reactions of lanthanum and chlorine (at 25°C),

$$La(s) + 3H^+(aq) \rightleftharpoons La^{3+}(aq) + \tfrac{3}{2}H_2(g) + 175{,}000 \text{ calories} \qquad (1)$$
$$La(s) \rightleftharpoons La(g) - 79{,}000 \qquad (2)$$
$$La(g) \rightleftharpoons La^{3+}(g) + 3e^- - 840{,}000 \qquad (3)$$
$$\tfrac{3}{2}Cl_2(g) + \tfrac{3}{2}H_2(g) \rightleftharpoons 3Cl^-(aq) + 3H^+(aq) + 94{,}000 \qquad (4)$$
$$\tfrac{3}{2}Cl_2(g) \rightleftharpoons 3Cl(g) - 76{,}000 \qquad (5)$$
$$3Cl(g) + 3e^- \rightleftharpoons 3Cl^-(g) + 262{,}000, \qquad (6)$$

where all the reactants and products are in the conventional standard states (Rossini, Wagman, Evans, Levine, and Jaffe, 1952). These can be combined to give the free energy of hydration of lanthanum chloride. Thus, adding reactions (1) and (4) and subtracting reaction (2), (3), (5), and (6), gives the hydration reaction

$$La^{3+}(g) + 3Cl^-(g) \rightleftharpoons La^{3+}(aq) + 3Cl^-(aq) + 1{,}002{,}000 \text{ calories.} \qquad (7)$$

The largest experimental term in the sum is the ionization potential of equation (3). This term is so much larger than any of the others that an informative value for the hydration energy of the lanthanum ion can be extracted from the data. If the free energy of hydration of the proton were known, it could be combined with other data to give the standard free energy for

$$\tfrac{3}{2}H_2(g) \rightleftharpoons 3H^+(aq) + 3e^-. \qquad (8)$$

* While the permittivity generally has been referred to in the foregoing as the *dielectric constant*, strictly speaking this should be done only in static fields of moderate intensities, where the permittivity is dependent solely upon the chemical composition and the density of the material and not on the field strength. In the case of high frequencies, and even in the case of optical frequencies, there is often a phase difference between the electric polarization and the dielectric displacement, so that the permittivity is not constant (see Böttcher, 1952).

Upon the basis of the Born model, the energy absorbed in reaction (8) is about 300,000 calories. It is argued below that this energy is much too large. But if one were to accept it as a rough approximation and to add equations (1) and (8), and to subtract equations (2) and (3), there would result,

$$La^{3+}(g) \rightleftharpoons La^{3+}(aq) + 794,000 \text{ calories.} \tag{9}$$

A smaller energy for reaction (8) would mean a larger energy for reaction (9).

Clearly, the origin of most of the very large energy release is the ionization potential of the lanthanum atom; it follows that approximately three electrons must again be associated with the lanthanum in the hydrated ion. Of course, the electrons also are associated with the water, because the net charge of the hydrated ion is plus three. No conceivable error in the energy of reaction (8) could invalidate this conclusion, which goes back to Bernal and Fowler (1933) who stated that, "the function of the ionizing medium is simply to return to the ion its missing electrons."

Other than the quantum-mechanical nature of the real ionization process, there is no fundamental conflict in the hydration of the cations with the spirit of the Born model. The Born discharge energy, $z^2 e^2 / 2r$, is, in fact, similar to the quantum-mechanical solution for the ionization potential of a hydrogen-like atom. The Born energies, however, are too large for radii derived from crystals (see page 64). With a crystallographic radius of 1.04A for La^{3+} (Zachariasen, 1954), the Born energy is 1,440,000 calories, which is 600,000 calories larger than the energy for reaction (3). To get agreement with experiment in this case, the radius would have to be about 1.8A, which is unreasonably large. The difficulty derives not so much from the uncertainty concerning the radii of the gaseous ions, as has been assumed by many workers, as it does from the crudity of the model. For the same reason, the excessive energy from the model is not necessarily the result of dielectric saturation.

In both the real process and the model, the ionization potential is a free energy content of the gaseous cation and separated negative charge. This free energy is released when the ion is submerged in water. A further implication, which is the key to Magnusson's critique, is that the nuclear charge of the cation must be well screened by water electrons. That is to say, at distances greater than its radius, the cation does not look like a point charge in a vacuum. Otherwise, the ionization energy in a vacuum would not be released as part of the hydration energy. The reality of screening a positive charge results, of course, from the wave nature of the electron and its indeterminacy in position.

Although the energies of the s electrons of noble-gas-type cations can be approximated roughly by simple Coulomb potentials (both in and out of a dielectric medium), there is no correspondence between the Born discharge of the anion and the real process. In fact, the discharge of the chloride ion (reaction 6) actually *absorbs* 87,000 cal / mole. The Born discharge energy of the gaseous anion is supposed to be the main term contributing to the anion hydration energy. This is the reason for the widely accepted view, based upon the division of energy indicated by the model, that an anion interacts with water somewhat more strongly than does a cation of the same size and charge. Combining reactions (4), (5), (6), and (8) yields the equation,

$$Cl^-(g) \rightleftharpoons Cl^-(aq) + 69,000 \text{ calories}, \tag{10}$$

for the hydration of the chloride ion. This energy is larger than that for a cation of comparable size. The calculated energy release for the anion is largely dependent upon the assumptions leading to an energy for equation (8). If the energy per mole of hydrogen ion for this reaction were to be as small as 31,000 calories (see below), the energy for reaction (10) would be zero.

The Born process is an artifice which is assumed to yield a path equivalent to the real path between initial and final states. One way to put the real anion through the Born process might be to excite it to a hypothetical state consisting of the atom surrounded by a spherical, conducting shell of negative charge with the classical anion radius and charge, e. The spherical shell of charge is removed by the Born discharge. The atom is placed in water and recharged with the spherical shell. Upon spontaneous collapse of the shell to form the real anion, the hypothetical excitation energy is assumed to be recovered and thereby cancelled from the process. Another way to accomplish this might be to surround the real ion with a shell of classical positive charge, submerge it, etc. The equivalence of the artifice and the real process is obviously a very questionable assumption.

One feature of the charging of the anion in water differs in a most significant way from the charging of the cation. The charge which is built up on the anion is an *electronic* charge. There is no mechanism for screening this charge which is analogous to the wave-mechanical screening of nuclear charges. The Born charging is a radially symmetrical process. If the discrete, particulate nature of the water medium now is taken into account in the description, it appears that the macroscopic dielectric constant of water cannot be applied isotropically around the anion. The field from the unscreened anion charge will, so to speak, shine out for appreciable distances between the nearest-neighbor water molecules, being modified only indirectly by the field from polarized water. The charging of the anion in water will require more energy than that postulated in the Born model, and the hydration energy will be less than that for a cation of the same effective Born radius. The over-all decrease in entropy of the water surrounding the anion will be greater than that for the cation.

An a priori calculation of the anion-charging process would be complicated, and the results no more convincing than the Born model, unless both the experimental free energies and entropies of hydration could be correlated with the model. With smaller anion-hydration energies, the energy absorbed by reaction (8) would be smaller (as mentioned above). If, as a reasonable minimum, the hydration model is required to return the electron-affinity energy, a lower limit of 31,000 calories per mole of hydrogen ion would be placed on the energy absorbed by reaction (8). Thus, the true value is believed to be between 31,000 and 100,000 cal / mole.

Almost all present theories of ionic entropies and the thermodynamic state of hydrate water are based entirely upon electrostatic determinations of the entropy. Implicit in the Born model is a measure of the entropy change, $-d(\Delta G) / dT$, which is a function of the dielectric permittivity. If the model includes saturation of the dielectric (which appears to be unavoidable), grave difficulty arises because the dependence of the permittivity function on temperature is unknown. It is noteworthy in this connection that no consistent treatment of both free energy and entropy has been achieved using electrostatic approaches (see Powell and Latimer, 1951; Laidler and Pegis, 1957; King, 1959; Noyes, 1962). If electrostatic models are inadequate, as Magnusson contends, the significance of the literature values for the individual ionic entropies would appear to be open to question. The individual free energies of hydration also may be quite uncertain because a potential change from a classical electrostatic calculation generally is valid only at 0°K, i.e., changes in the thermal energies of the species in the system are not considered. The equating of potential energy and free energy in the Born model is possible only because the change in the thermal energy of the water in the electric field is contained in the permittivity-temperature relation. If there are thermal changes in the water and the ions which cannot be assigned to a permittivity function, then the energies of the individual ions cannot be obtained from the Born model.

To avoid the ambiguity of the Born model regarding the discrete structure of water, many workers have attempted to account for variations in the interactions of dissolved ions and water using the point-charge dipole model (see above). The number of water molecules bound to the ion then is postulated to depend upon the binding of the water in the body of the solvent. As noted above, the criteria for ion hydration generally have been the Bernal-Fowler criterion that the ion-dipole association energy must exceed the (negative) potential energy of the water molecule in the bulk water (computed to be 15,300 cal / mole by Bernal and Fowler, 1933), or, more recently, the Harris-O'Konski criterion that it must exceed the hydrogen-bond energy (computed to be 7,700 cal / mole* by Harris and O'Konski, 1957). As pointed out above, however, these electrostatic criteria could be applicable only at 0°K, for the entropies of the water in the ion-bound and water-bound states at ordinary temperatures are not taken into account.

Although the almost exact factor of two between the numerical values for the potential energy of the water molecule and for the energy of hydrogen bonds in

---

* The latest determination of the hydrogen-bond energy by infrared spectroscopy (on the assumption that there are between 8 and 12 nearest-neighbors of a water molecule in the closely-packed liquid structure) gives the much lower value of 3,700 to 4,500 cal / mole (Buijs and Choppin, 1963). For a discussion of the difficult problem of the hydrogen-bond energy, see Coulson (1957) and Pimentel and McClellan (1960).

bulk water is somewhat fortuitous, there is a basic reason for expecting the values of the different energies chosen as comparative criteria by Bernal and Fowler, on the one hand, and Harris and O'Konski, on the other, to differ by a factor of two. Thus, according to the model of Bernal and Fowler, the coordination of a water molecule to a cation involves a net-breaking of two hydrogen bonds, whereas the discussion of Harris and O'Konski implies that only one hydrogen bond is broken in this process. Apart from the more basic question of the validity of the point-charge dipole model, these different assumptions lead to quite different expectations. Thus, as noted above, Bernal and Fowler postulated that ions with crystallographic radii greater than 1.6A (including the monatomic ions Cs^+, Cl^-, Br^-, and I^-) do not bind water, whereas the assumption of Harris and O'Konski leads one to expect hydration for ions with radii as large as 2.8A (which includes all the monatomic ions). The point-charge dipole model, accordingly, does not appear to be consistent with experimental hydration energies. It should be noted in this connection that Bernal and Fowler found it necessary to double the potential energy of the water molecule in bulk in computing hydration energies.

According to Magnusson (1963), hydration must depend upon free energy. If the free energy (or activity) of the hydrate water is less than that of the water species which can bond to the ion, more water will tend to add to the ion to reach an equilibrium state. A proper calculation of the free energy from electrostatic potentials would be complex and would require assumptions for the heat capacities. More importantly, if the real bonds have a covalent stabilization, a dipole calculation cannot be correct.

Data on the 1-1 fluoride-complex ion with noble-gas-type cations have been examined for information on the short-range ion-ion and water-ion interactions (Magnusson, 1963). It appeared reasonable to correlate the free energies and entropies of formation of 2+, 3+, and 4+ cations with relatively simple equations containing electrostatic terms. A small, constant free energy term appears to be associated with an entropy change characteristic of that for bound water going to liquid water. This small term was assigned to the process of removing hydrate water from the internuclear axis as the cation and anion approached contact.

By contrast, if the integral free energy of hydration, as determined by the Born model, were the sum of all the cation-water dipole interactions, the free energy for the removal of one water molecule would not be small. That the free energy is small and is independent of the cation charge would seem to signify that a water dipole is not interacting with the vacuum field of a point charge. A further significance of the small free energy is that the hydrate water must be in equilibrium with the bulk water.

The above conclusion is valid regardless of whether a water molecule is removed from one or both of the ions, or not at all. If the latter were true, it would mean that a coordination site was available on both the cation and the anion. The affinities of the separated ions for water then would be satisfied with less than the sterically permissible number of water molecules. If a water molecule is removed from either or both of the ions, the process would be occurring near equilibrium, and the effective coordination numbers of the separated ions could not be integral. That is to say, one would find an equilibrium mixture of ions holding N and $N - 1$ coordinated water molecules, where N is the sterically permissible number. This interpretation is consistent with a screened-nuclear-charge (covalent) model of the cation, in which the screening may be nearly as good as with one less water molecule.

The role of the anion is more uncertain. It is an interesting speculation that the empirical exponential attractive term (see Magnusson, 1963; equation 9) between the cation and the anion may reflect that part of the field of the anion which is not screened (Magnusson, 1963, 1964). Part or all of the free energy for removing or loosening water from the anion may be contained in this term. An alternative, or additional, explanation may be derived from the probability that the entropy of the hydrate water of the anion is considerably less than the entropy of the hydrate water of a cation of comparable size and charge (see above). At $0°K$, the free energy for removing one water molecule from the hydrated anion would be relatively large. At ordinary temperatures the free energy would be much less, possibly near zero.

Whereas Magnusson deduced that ion-water interactions probably involve covalent binding from thermodynamic considerations, Bergqvist and Forslind (1962) and Forslind (1963) have been led to the same conclusion by nuclear magnetic resonance studies (as noted above). Thus, Forslind (1963) finds many of the assumptions of the electrostatic models concerning the orientation of a water molecule toward a dissolved ion to be quite arbitrary. He feels that there is little or no support for the idea that the over-all dipole moment of a free water molecule would determine its orientation toward a polarizable free ion.* Forslind suggests that there is even less reason to expect this relationship to hold in the case of a water molecule incorporated into a lattice, where the polarization of the molecule already is determined essentially by cooperation with its neighbors.

If the interaction between the dissolved ion and the water is sufficiently strong to lead to the formation of a new molecular species, Forslind contends that the interaction will not be determined upon the basis of the dipole orientations of the interacting particles, but that it will occur along directions of water and ion hybridization configurations that correspond to the least energy for the formation of ordinary covalent bonds. This relationship is believed to apply regardless of whether or not the complex formation depends upon hydrogen-bonding. On the other hand, if the ion retains its individuality in the dissolved state, it is proposed that its directions of polarization will be determined by the instantaneous configurations of the surrounding water

_____

* In this connection, Vaslow's (1963) calculations (see page 56) also support the idea that water molecules orient around ions according to the directions of their electron orbitals rather than according to the direction of their over-all dipole moment.

molecules in the lattice, which again have little relationship to the over-all dipole moments of the molecules (Forslind, 1963).

Consequences for proton exchanges

THE STRUCTURE-BROKEN REGION. The fact that many fixed charges in biological interfaces are of low individual field strength ensures the existence of a region in which appreciable structure-breaking occurs. This will be true regardless of whether the structure-breaking always occurs beyond the primary hydration shell or whether it sometimes occurs in the immediate ionic vicinity. Thus, a "thawed," but not necessarily continuous, envelope in which hydrogen-bonding is poorer than in ordinary water will surround the hydration crust of membrane interfaces at which appreciable electrostatic fields exist. Accordingly, it can be concluded that these regions will act as insulators, insofar as proton exchanges by isotropic volume conduction between interfacial regions and the circumambient cytoplasmic matrix are concerned.

THE REGION OF IMMOBILIZATION, POLARIZATION, AND ELECTROSTRICTION. In spite of the decrease in thermal vibration amplitudes, hydrogen-bonding between nearest-neighbor water molecules surrounding ions would not be expected to be promoted,* for adjacent molecules have unfavorable orientations with regard to the possibility of hybrid alignment and efficient orbital overlap (see Forslind, 1952). This tends to be borne out by the decrease in dielectric relaxation time in increasingly concentrated solutions of strong inorganic electrolytes, which is interpreted as a result of decreased hydrogen-bonding (Hasted, Ritson, and Collie, 1948; Haggis, Hasted, and Buchanan, 1952; Hasted and Roderick, 1958). The depression of the dielectric constant was regarded by the same workers as being caused by restriction of the rotation of the coordinated water dipoles—the stronger the dipole coupling, the more restricted the rotation. Bergqvist and Forslind (1962) ascribed the chemical shifts of the proton resonance lines to the combined effects of hydrogen-bond rupture and distortion polarization. A remarkable parallelism is shown by the curves for the molar dielectric relaxation depression, for the molar dielectric constant depression, and for the molal proton magnetic resonance shifts of the alkali-metal ions and halide ions.

Since hydrogen-bonding between water molecules interacting with ions probably is hindered, one also expects ions to hinder conduction by excess and defect proton transfers, an effect alluded to briefly by Onsager (1945). On the basis of conductivity and dialysis studies, Suhrmann and Wiedersich (1953) have, indeed, shown that cations hinder proton transport; the stronger the electric field of the cation (i.e., the smaller its radius and greater its charge), the greater the hindrance. On the other hand, the same workers have shown that protons are unrestrained in moving through the hydration sphere

* However, hydrogen-bonding between nearest-neighbor water molecules and hydroxyl and hydronium ions are strengthened and proton jumps facilitated (see Ackermann, 1957).

73

of anions, or, at least, that the presence of anions does not hinder proton exchanges. The lack of hindrance is believed to be due to the weaker polarizing and immobilizing of first-hydration-sphere water molecules by the anions.

In recent years almost all the evidence relating to the effects of ions on proton transfer rates has come from nuclear magnetic resonance studies. The early NMR studies by Shoolery and Alder (1955) suggested that many diamagnetic ions do not hinder proton transfers in their neighborhood to a significant degree. Although there are three distinct species of water molecules—near an anion, near a cation and near other water molecules distant from added electrolytes—only a single proton resonance line was observed in concentrated salt solutions. Except for Al^{3+}, Be^{2+}, and the most concentrated $ZnCl_2$ solutions (12.5 M), the line was not broadened noticeably relative to the broadening observed for pure water.* This was taken to indicate that the time of exchange of those protons in the neighborhood of an ion with those relatively far away from any ion is so fast (i.e., relative to the resolving power of the technique) that only the average proton resonance, i.e., exchange-narrowing, is observed. In other words, the line represents an average of the chemical shifts arising from the three different environments. Accordingly, it was concluded that the proton exchange rate between the three different environments in salt solutions was faster than 10,000 / second.

The more recent studies of proton resonance shifts† in alkali-halide solutions by Fabricand and Goldberg (1961), Hindman (1962), and Bergqvist and Forslind (1962) were carried out with greatly improved instrumental resolution and with field corrections for the bulk diamagnetic susceptibility of the solution. Although the results of Shoolery and Alder were confirmed qualitatively, inasmuch as only one proton resonance line was observed, the significance of this finding for proton exchange rates is complicated by several factors.

Measurements of nuclear magnetic relaxation times of protons in aqueous solutions of Mn^{2+} ions indicated that some type of chemical exchange involving the protons took place, giving a mean lifetime of the protons in the hydration sphere of about 2.5×10^{-8} sec at 27°C (Bernheim, Brown, Gutowsky, and Woessner, 1959). The results did not indicate whether the exchange involved only the protons or whether whole water molecules as such participated. However, the low activation energy of only 8,400 cal / mole found for the exchange process suggested that it was mainly chemical exchanging of solvent protons with those in the hydrated Mn^{2+} ion. Recently, how-

---

* The magnetic field dependence of the line width in the $AlCl_3$ solutions indicated that a proton exchange rate of 100 / sec was responsible for the broadening, while in the case of the $ZnCl_2$ and $BeCl_2$ solutions, the high viscosity appeared to be the chief factor responsible for the increased line width.

† For further material relating to the topics discussed in the remainder of this chapter, see the discussion of the German Bunsen-Society for Physical Chemistry, Marl in Westfalen, October, 1962, titled "Magnetische Kernresonanzspektroskopie ihre Anwendungen und Möglichkeiten in der Physikalischen Chemie;" *Ber. deutsche Bunsen-Gesellschaft*, March, 1963.

ever, it has been found that for paramagnetic ions the rate of exchange of the coordinated water molecules themselves with bulk water is much greater than the rate of chemical exchange of protons in bulk water. Thus Pearson, Palmer, Anderson, and Allred (1960) pointed out that the measured proton exchange rates in manganous-ion solutions did not result from a chemical shift but rather from the exchange of whole water molecules. This was affirmed by Swift and Connick (1962), who found the rate of exchange of oxygen between the first coordination sphere of manganous ions and the bulk water to be essentially identical with the corresponding rate of proton exchange (Bernheim, Brown, Gutowsky, and Woessner, 1959).

Connick and co-workers (Connick and Poulson, 1959; Connick and Stover, 1961; Swift and Connick, 1962) have studied the relative effectiveness of various paramagnetic cations in broadening the resonance of the O^{17} nucleus in O^{17}-enriched water. The transverse relaxation of the resonance occurs almost entirely in the first sphere of coordinated water for all the cations studied except the chromic ion. The rate of exchange of water molecules in the bulk solution with those in the first coordinated sphere about paramagnetic cations is relatively high, ranging from 2.7×10^4 / sec for Ni^{2+} to 2×10^8 / sec for Cu^{2+}. These results were deemed to be consistent with an appreciable crystal-field effect on the rate of exchange of water molecules.

Exchange of methanol molecules between the solvent shell of paramagnetic ions in methanol solution and the bulk methanol solvent also has been shown to be much faster than the exchange of protons between molecules in the two environments (Pearson, Palmer, Anderson, and Allred, 1960; Luz and Meiboom, 1963b).

Since the charged groups at membrane interfaces would not be expected to facilitate proton transfers, it is pertinent to inquire whether conduction by proton exchanges would be facilitated to the same degree throughout the hydration crust of membrane interfaces, or whether it would differ in rate according to the distribution of ion-coordinated water. Since charged groups that are part of the membrane (such as $-COO^-$, $>PO_4^-$, and $-NH_3^+$) generally have low field strengths, it is a fair guess, based primarily upon Suhrmann and Wiedersich's (1953) findings, that proton transfers through first-hydration-sphere water will not be hindered. All such attached groups, in fact, probably lead to net structure-breaking. On the other hand, when such polar groups are not ionized they hydrogen-bond with greater or lesser strength to neighboring water molecules and probably facilitate proton transfers through the hydration crust. Since the charge distributions on such groups would be expected to fluctuate rapidly (Kirkwood and Shumaker, 1952), any effects of these groups on the structure of, and the proton transfer rate through, neighboring water would be averaged out over all groups. Upon this basis, one might expect such groups to give a net facilitation of proton transfers through nearest-neighbor water molecules.

The most important factor in connection with proton transfer rates in the hydration crust probably is the presence of —CH₂— groups attached to or in the vicinity of all the fixed charges in membrane interfaces. These groups still can exert about the same influence on the energy states of water as they do in the absence of the neighboring charge, although the exact local structure of water in their neighborhood might be different from that in solutions of pure hydrocarbons (Némethy and Scheraga, 1962b). Accordingly, —CH₂— groups probably tend to provide hydrogen-bonded "short circuits" around regions in which water structure is altered by charged groups. This effect has been shown convincingly in recent experiments. For example, the rate of deprotonation of the $MeNH_3^+$ ion is faster than that of the NH_4^+ ion, even though the methyl group leads to partial steric blocking of the nitrogen atom (see below and Eigen and co-workers, cited in Némethy and Scheraga, 1962a). The same effect leads to an increased rate of recombination of HO^- ions with substituted amines over that which is achieved with ammonium ions (Eigen and Schwarz, 1963).

Protolysis reactions of the ammonium ion and of the three methyl ammonium ions in aqueous solution have been studied in considerable detail by Meiboom and his collaborators (see Luz and Meiboom, 1963a, for references). The dominant reactions in the pH range 3 to 5, at amine concentrations above 0.01 M are

$$R_3NH^+ + NR_3 \xrightarrow{k_1} R_3N + H^+NR_3 \qquad (11)$$

$$R_3NH^+ + \overset{H}{O}H + \overset{H}{O}H + \overset{H}{O}H + \cdots + NR_3 \xrightarrow{k_2}$$

$$R_3N + \overset{H}{H}O + \overset{H}{H}O + \overset{H}{H}O + \cdots + H^+NR_3, \qquad (12)$$

where R denotes either a methyl group or a hydrogen atom.

Nuclear magnetic resonance differentiates between reactions (11) and (12) because it is possible to determine independently the average residence times of protons on methylated and unmethylated ammonium ions and on water molecules from the width of their resonance lines. It was found that more than 90% of the proton exchange for the trimethylammonium ion occurs by transfer through water molecules (equation 12) whereas for the ammonium ion the greater part of the exchange occurs by direct reaction with ammonia (equation 11). The rates of the reactions of equations (11) and (12) are comparable for the methyl- and dimethylammonium ions. Accordingly, it would appear that the increased rate of protolysis of $MeNH_3^+$ over NH_4^+ has its basis in the cluster-promoting effect of methyl groups, which provide improved pathways for proton exchange through the ion-coordinated water and the intermediate structure-broken regions. The more methyl groups present, the better the hydrogen-bond pathways, whereas in the absence of a methyl group the speed of exchange is reduced and depends largely upon direct interactions between the exchanging species.

In earlier studies (references in Luz and Meiboom, 1963a) it was not possible to decide how many water molecules were involved in the reaction of equation (12) because direct proton exchanges from one water molecule to another do not result in changes in proton resonance frequency and so do not contribute to the width of the water line. However, as noted above, the rate of direct exchange between water molecules can be determined in O^{17}-enriched water (Meiboom, 1961). Thus, the number of water molecules taking part in the reaction of equation (12) can be measured by comparing the appreciable excess width of the water line in O^{17}-enriched water with that in non-enriched water. This has been done by Luz and Meiboom (1963a) who investigated the reaction

$$Me_3NH^+ + nH_2O + NMe_3 \xrightarrow{k_3} Me_3N + nH_2O + H^+NMe_3 \qquad (13)$$

in O^{17}-enriched solutions containing variable amounts of trimethylammonium ion-trimethylamine buffer. The measurements were carried out at proton concentrations between pH 6 and 8 to prevent those excess and defect proton exchanges which occur only between water molecules from dominating over the proton exchanges involving the buffer components (equation 13). Since the value of k_3 is 3.3×10^8 liter / mole-sec, and nk_3 was found to be 3.03×10^8 liter / mole-sec, it follows that only one water molecule (which is probably part of the solvent shell of the ion) is involved in the transfer reaction of equation (13).

In view of the above considerations, it can be postulated that one of the functions of the ethyl chains of the serine, choline, and cholamine residues of the phospholipids and of the methyl groups of choline in biological membranes is to provide one or more near-neighbor cluster-promoting groups for each ionogenic group and its counterions. The author has proposed that in the closed configuration of biological membranes many of the terminal polar residues of phospholipids in regions between the pillar bases have left the aqueous phase by bending back into the lipid phase between the hydrocarbon chains. The reduction of the number of hydrogen-bonded short circuits for proton transfers around phosphate groups, as a result of this action, together with the much lower degree of hydration of membrane interfaces in the closed configuration, could be important factors in the greater stability of the closed configuration over the open one (see chaps. 7 and 8, vol. I, Kavanau, 1964).

The sign of the *net* effect of monatomic *counterions* on proton exchange rates in the hydration crust of membranes is difficult to assess. Negatively charged counterions would be expected to have a net-facilitating effect, for whereas in the unbound condition they would not hinder proton transfers, when coordinated either loosely or closely to fixed membrane cations they would tend to counteract any hindrance of proton exchanges exerted by these charged groups. On the other hand, positively charged counterions might have a net-hindering effect, although it probably would be very small. Those free cations which would tend to hinder proton exchanging the most (Mg^{2+} and Ca^{2+}) are just the ones that should tend to have their charges screened most effectively by specific ion-pairing and site-binding to fixed anions (see chap. 7, vol. I, Kavanau, 1964). All interactions between counter-cations and fixed anions at membrane interfaces would tend to promote hydrogen-bonding, so that one component of the effects of counter-cations would be expected to facilitate proton exchanges. Whatever the sign of the net effect of all monatomic counterions, its magnitude probably would be small.

It can be concluded, then, that the over-all effect of the hydration crust of icebergs and soft ice at membrane interfaces is to facilitate proton transfers along the interfaces (particularly in the open configuration). Charged groups at membrane interfaces probably provide an external "insulating" structure-broken region through which proton transfers occur less readily than in either the interface or the surrounding matrix. In membranes undergoing propagated transformations, the existence of potential gradients along the interfaces (resulting from local proton-activity changes) probably also would favor proton transfers longitudinally within the hydration crust, by virtue of field effects on the alignments of the participating dipoles.

REFERENCES

ACKERMANN, TH., 1957. Disc. Faraday Soc. **24**:180.
———, 1961. Z. Physik. Chem. **27**:253.
ARANOW, R. H. and L. WITTEN, 1958. J. Chem. Phys. **28**:405.
——— and ———, 1960. J. Phys. Chem. **64**:1643.
——— and ———, 1961. J. Chem. Phys. **34**:1504.
ARNOLD, J. T. and M. E. PACKARD, 1951. Phys. Rev. **83**:210; J. Chem. Phys. **19**:1608.
ASMUS, E., 1949. Z. Naturforsch. **4a**:589.
AUERBACH, P., P. DUCROS, and X. PARE, 1960. Compt. Rend. **250**:322.
AUTY, R. P. and R. H. COLE, 1952. J. Chem. Phys. **20**:1309.

BACON, G. E., 1959. *in* Hydrogen Bonding (D. Hadzi and H. W. Thompson, eds.) Pergamon Press, London.
BALAZS, E. A., A. A. BOTHNER-BY, and J. GERGELY, 1959. J. Mol. Biol. **1**:147.
BARNES, W. H., 1929. Proc. Roy. Soc. **A125**:670.
BASCOMBE, K. N. and R. P. BELL, 1957. Disc. Faraday Soc. **24**:158.
BEAUMONT, R. H., H. CHIHARA, and J. A. MORRISON, 1961. J. Chem. Phys. **34**:1456.
BECKEY, H. D., 1958. Rept. on the Fourth Internat. Congress on Electron-Microscopy, Springer-Verlag, Berlin.
BENJAMIN, L. and G. C. BENSON, 1963. J. Phys. Chem. **67**:858.
BENSON, S. W. and C. S. COPELAND, 1963. J. Phys. Chem. **67**:1194.
BERENDSEN, H. J., 1960. Biol. Bull. **119**:287.
———, 1962. J. Chem. Phys. **36**:3297; Thesis, Univ. of Groningen.
BERGQVIST, M. S. and E. FORSLIND, 1962. Acta Chem. Scand. **16**:2069.
BERNAL, J. D., 1959. *in* Hydrogen Bonding (D. Hadzi and H. W. Thompson, eds.), Pergamon Press, London.
——— and R. H. FOWLER, 1933. J. Chem. Phys. **1**:515.
BERNHEIM, R. A., T. H. BROWN, H. S. GUTOWSKY, and D. E. WOESSNER, 1959. J. Chem. Phys. **30**:950.
BERTIE, J. E., L. D. CALVERT, and E. WHALLEY, 1963. J. Chem. Phys. **38**:840.
BEURSKENS, P. T. and G. A. JEFFREY, 1964. J. Chem. Phys. **40**:906.
BEURSKENS-KERSSEN, G., G. A. JEFFREY, and R. K. MCMULLAN, 1963. J. Chem. Phys. **39**:3311.
BJERRUM, N., 1952. Science **115**:385.
BLACKMAN, M. and N. D. LISGARTEN, 1957. Proc. Roy. Soc. **A239**:93.
——— and ———, 1958. Adv. Physics **7**:189.
BOCKRIS, J. O'M, 1949. Quart. Rev. **3**:173.
BOLT, G. H., 1954. Thesis, Cornell University.
———, 1955. J. Colloid Sci. **10**:206.
BOOTH, F., 1951. J. Chem. Phys. **19**:391, 821, 1327, 1615.
———, 1955. J. Chem. Phys. **23**:453.
BORN, M., 1920. Z. Physik. **1**:45.
BÖTTCHER, C. F., 1952. Theory of Electric Polarization, Elsevier, New York.

Brady, G. W., 1958. J. Chem. Phys. **28**:464; **29**:1371.

————, 1960. J. Chem. Phys. **33**:1079.

———— and J. T. Krause, 1957. J. Chem. Phys. **27**:304.

———— and W. J. Romanow, 1960. J. Chem. Phys. **32**:306.

Bridgman, P. W., 1912. Proc. Amer. Acad. **47**:441.

————, 1935. J. Chem. Phys. **3**:597.

————, 1937. J. Chem. Phys. **5**:964.

Buckingham, A. D., 1957. Disc. Faraday Soc. **24**:151.

Buijs, K. and G. R. Choppin, 1963. J. Chem. Phys. **39**:2035.

Burnelle, L. and C. A. Coulson, 1957. Trans. Faraday Soc. **49**:217.

Burton, E. F. and W. F. Oliver, 1935. Proc. Roy. Soc. **A153**:166.

Busig, W. R. and D. F. Hornig, 1961. J. Phys. Chem. **65**:284.

Cannon, C. G., 1958. Disc. Faraday Soc. **25**:59.

Chadwell, H. M., 1927. Chem. Rev. **4**:375.

Choppin, G. R. and K. Buijs, 1963. J. Chem. Phys. **39**:2042.

Claussen, W. F., 1951. J. Chem. Phys. **19**:259, 662, 1425.

———— and M. F. Polglas, 1952. J. Amer. Chem. Soc. **74**:4817.

Cohan, N. V., M. Cotti, J. V. Iribarne, and M. Weissmann, 1962. Trans. Faraday Soc. **58**:490.

Cohen, M. H. and D. Turnbull, 1959. J. Chem. Phys. **31**:1164.

Collie, C. H., J. B. Hasted, and D. M. Ritson, 1948. Proc. Phys. Soc. **60**:145.

Connick, R. E. and D. N. Fiat, 1963. J. Chem. Phys. **39**:1349.

———— and R. E. Poulson, 1959. J. Chem. Phys. **30**:759.

———— and E. D. Stover, 1961. J. Phys. Chem. **65**:2075.

Conture, A. M. and K. J. Laidler, 1957. Canad. J. Chem. **35**:207.

Conway, B. E., J. O'M. Bockris, and H. Linton, 1956. J. Chem. Phys. **24**:834.

Coulson, C. A., 1957. Research **10**:149; also *in* Hydrogen Bonding (D. Hadzi and H. W. Thompson, eds.), Pergamon Press, London, 1959.

———— and U. Danielsson, 1954. Ark. Fysik **8**:239, 254.

———— and D. H. Everett, 1940. Trans. Faraday Soc. **36**: 633.

Cox, W. M. and J. H. Wolfenden, 1934. Proc. Roy. Soc. **A145**:475.

Danford, M. D. and H. A. Levy, 1962. J. Amer. Chem. Soc. **84**:3965.

Darmois, E., 1946. J. Chim. Phys. (Memoires II).

Daszkiewicz, O. K., J. W. Hennel, B. Lubas, and T. W. Szczepkowski, 1963. Nature **200**:1006.

Davies, J. T. and E. K. Rideal, 1961. Interfacial Phenomena, Academic Press, New York.

Debye, P., 1929. Polar Molecules, Chemical Catalog Co., Inc., New York.

———— and H. Falkenhagen, 1928. Physik. Z. **29**:121, 401; Z. Elektrochem. **34**:562.

Denbigh, K. G., 1940. Trans. Faraday Soc. **36**:936.

Depireux, J. and D. Williams, 1962. Nature **195**:699.

Derjaguin, B. V., 1936. Nature **138**:330.

———— and V. V. Karassev, 1957. Proc. Second Internat. Congress of Surface Activity **3**:531.

———— and A. S. Titjevskaya, 1957. Proc. Second Internat. Congress of Surface Activity **1**:211, 254.

DERVICHIAN, D. G., 1946. Trans. Faraday Soc. 42B:180.

DEWAR, J., 1905. Chem. News 91:216.

DIAMOND, R. M., 1958. J. Amer. Chem. Soc. 80:4808.

———, 1963. J. Phys. Chem. 67:2513.

DINTZIS, H. M., J. L. ONCLEY, and R. M. FUOSS, 1954. Proc. Nat. Acad. Sci. 40:62.

DOLE, M. and A. D. McLAREN, 1947. J. Amer. Chem. Soc. 69:651.

DONOHUE, J., 1957. in Molecular Structure and Biological Specificity (L. Pauling and H. A. Itano, eds.), Waverly Press, Inc., Baltimore.

D'ORAZIO, L. A. and R. H. WOOD, 1963. J. Phys. Chem. 67:1435.

DORSEY, N. E., 1940. Properties of Ordinary Water Substance, Reinhold, New York.

DOUGLASS, D. C., H. L. FRISCH, and E. W. ANDERSON, 1960. Biochim. Biophys. Acta 44:401.

DOWELL, L. G. and A. P. RINFRET, 1960. Nature 188:1144.

DROST-HANSEN, W., 1956. Naturwiss. 43:512.

DUCROS, P., 1960. Bull. Soc. Franç. Mineral. Crist. 83:85.

——— and M. DUPONT, 1962. Compt. Rend. 254:1409.

DUNCAN, A. B. and J. A. POPLE, 1953. Trans. Faraday Soc. 49:217.

DUNITZ, J. D., 1963. Nature 197:860.

ECK, C. L. VAN P. VAN, H. MENDEL, and J. FAHRENFORT, 1958. Proc. Roy. Soc. A247:472.

EIGEN, M., 1961. in Advances in the Chemistry of the Coordination Compounds (S. Kirschner, ed.), Macmillan, New York.

———, 1963. Pure Appl. Chem. 6:97.

——— and L. DE MAEYER, 1956. Z. Elektrochem. 60:1037.

——— and ———, 1958. Proc. Roy. Soc. A247:505.

——— and ———, 1959. in The Structure of Electrolytic Solutions (W. J. Hamer, ed.), John Wiley & Sons, Inc., New York.

——— and G. SCHWARZ, 1963. Abstr., Meeting Amer. Chem. Soc., New York, Sept. 9–13.

——— and E. WICKE, 1951. Z. Elektrochem. 55:344.

EISENBERG, D. and C. A. COULSON, 1963. Nature 199:368.

EISENMAN, G., 1961. in Symposium on Membrane Transport and Metabolism (A. Kleinzeller and A. Kotzk, eds.), Academic Press, New York.

———, 1962. Biophys. J. 2(Suppl.):259.

ELEY, D. D., 1939. Trans. Faraday Soc. 35:1281, 1421.

——— and M. G. EVANS, 1938. Trans. Faraday Soc. 34:1093.

ERRERA, J., J. TH. OVERBEEK, and H. SACK, 1935. J. Chim. Phys. 32:681.

EUCKEN, A., 1947. Nachr. Ges. Wiss. Göttingen, p. 33.

———, 1948. Z. Elektrochem. 51:6.

——— and M. EIGEN, 1951. Z. Elektrochem. 55:343.

EVERETT, D. H., 1957. in Discussion, Disc. Faraday Soc. 24:216, 220, 229.

FABRICAND, B. P. and S. GOLDBERG, 1961. J. Chem. Phys. 34:1624.

FAJANS, K. and O. JOHNSON, 1942. J. Amer. Chem. Soc. 64:668.

FEATES, F. S. and D. J. IVES, 1956. J. Chem. Soc. 1956:2798.

FERNÁNDEZ-MORÁN, H., 1960. in Fast Fundamental Transfer Processes in Aqueous

Biomolecular Systems (F. O. Schmitt, ed.), Dept. of Biol., Mass. Inst. Tech., Cambridge.

FINBAK, C. and H. VIERVOLL, 1943. Tidsskr. Kjemi, Bergvesen Met. 3:36.

FISHER, I. Z., 1962. J. Structural Chem. 3:604.

FORSLIND, E., 1952. Acta Polytechnica 115:9.

———, 1953. Proc. Second Internat. Congr. Rheology, Butterworths, London.

———, 1963. Personal communication.

FRANK, H. S., 1958. Proc. Roy. Soc. A247:481.

———, 1963a. Nat. Acad. Sci.–Nat. Res. Council Pub. 42:141.

———, 1963b. J. Phys. Chem. 67:1554.

——— and M. W. EVANS, 1945. J. Chem. Phys. 13:507.

——— and A. S. QUIST, 1961. J. Chem. Phys. 34:604.

——— and A. L. ROBINSON, 1940. J. Chem. Phys. 8:933.

——— and W.-Y. WEN, 1957. Disc. Faraday Soc. 24:133.

FREED, S., 1942. Rev. Modern Poys. 14:105.

FREUNDLICH, H., 1932. Kapillarchemie, Vol. II, Akad. Verlag, Leipzig.

FRICKE, H., 1953. J. Phys. Chem. 57:934.

FUOSS, R. M. and L. ONSAGER, 1955. Proc. Nat. Acad. Sci. 41:274.

——— and ———, 1957. J. Phys. Chem. 61:668.

GIERER, A. and K. WIRTZ, 1949. Ann. Phys. Leipzig 6:257.

——— and ———, 1952. J. Phys. Chem. 56:914.

GILLESPIE, R. J., 1957. Disc. Faraday Soc. 24:230.

GINELL, R., 1961. J. Chem. Phys. 34:992, 1249, 2174.

GJALDBAEK, J. C. and J. H. HILDEBRAND, 1950. J. Amer. Chem. Soc. 72:1077.

GLEW, D. W. and R. E. ROBERTSON, 1956. J. Phys. Chem. 60:332.

GLUECKHAUF, E., 1955. Trans. Faraday Soc. 51:1235.

GRAHAM, J., G. F. WALKER, and G. W. WEST, 1964. J. Chem. Phys. 40:540.

GRAHAME, D. C., 1950. J. Chem. Phys. 18:903.

GRAHN, R., 1961. Ark. Fysik 19:147.

———, 1962. Ark. Fysik 21:1, 13, 81.

GRÄNICHER, H., 1958. Proc. Roy. Soc. A247:453.

GRAY, G. W., 1962. Molecular Structure and the Properties of Liquid Crystals, Academic Press, New York.

GRIMISON, A., 1963. J. Phys. Chem. 67:962.

GRJOTHEIM, K. and J. KROGH-MOE, 1954. Acta Chem. Scand. 8:1193.

GROTTHUSS, C. J. VON, 1806. Ann. Chem. 58:54.

GRUNBERG, L. and H. A. NISSAN, 1949. Trans. Faraday Soc. 45:125.

GUGGENHEIM, E. A., 1929. J. Phys. Chem. 33:842.

———, 1930. J. Phys. Chem. 34:1540.

GURNEY, R. W., 1953. Ionic Processes in Solution, McGraw-Hill, New York.

GUTOWSKY, H. S. and A. SAIKA, 1953. J. Chem. Phys. 21:1688.

HAGGIS, G. H., J. B. Hasted, and T. J. BUCHANAN, 1952. J. Chem. Phys. 20:1452.

HALL, L., 1948. Phys. Rev. 73:775.

HAMMERSTEN, E., 1924. Biochem. Z. 144:383.

HARDY, W. B., 1927. J. Gen. Physiol. 8:641.

HARRIS, F. E. and B. J. ALDER, 1953. J. Chem. Phys. 21:1031.
―――― and C. T. O'KONSKI, 1957. J. Phys. Chem. 61:310.
HASTED, J. B., D. M. RITSON, and C. H. COLLIE, 1948. J. Chem. Phys. 16:1.
―――― and G. W. RODERICK, 1958. J. Chem. Phys. 29:17.
HAUSER, E. A., 1931. J. Rheology 2:5.
HAVESTADT, L. and R. FRICK, 1930. Z. Anorg. Allg. Chem. 188:357.
―――― and ――――, 1931. Z. Anorg. Allg. Chem. 196:120.
HAZLEHURST, T. H. and H. A. NEVILLE, 1940. J. Phys. Chem. 44:592.
HEARST, J. E. and J. VINOGRAD, 1961. Proc. Nat. Acad. Sci. 47:825, 1005.
HECHTER, O., T. WITTSTRUCK, N. MCNIVEN, and G. LESTER, 1960. Proc. Nat. Acad. Sci. 46:783.
HELLER, W., 1942. Rev. Modern Phys. 14:390.
HEPLER, L. G., 1957. J. Phys. Chem. 61:1426.
HIGDON, W. T. and J. D. ROBINSON, 1962. J. Chem. Phys. 37:1161.
HINDMAN, J. C., 1962. J. Chem. Phys. 36:1000.
HONJO, G., N. KITAMURA, K. SHIMAOKA, and K. MIHAMA, 1956. J. Phys. Soc. Japan 11:527.
―――― and K. SHIMAOKA, 1957. Acta Cryst. 10:710.
HOOD, G. C., O. REDLICH, and C. A. REILLY, 1954. J. Chem. Phys. 22:2067.
HORNIG, D. F., H. F. WHITE, and E. P. REDING, 1958. Spectrochim. Acta 12:338.
HÜCKEL, E., 1928. Z. Elektrochem. 34:546.
HUGGINS, C. H., G. C. PIMENTEL, and J. N. SHOOLERY, 1955. J. Chem. Phys. 23:1244.
HUGHES, D. J., H. PALEVSKY, W. KLEY, and E. TUNKELO, 1960. Phys. Rev. 119:872.
HUNT, J. P. and H. TAUBE, 1951. J. Chem. Phys. 19:602.

JACKMAN, L. M., 1959. Nuclear Magnetic Resonance Spectroscopy, Pergamon Press, London.
JACOBSON, B., 1953a. Nature 172:666.
――――, 1953b. Rev. Sci. Instr. 24:949.
――――, 1955. Acta Chem. Scand. 9:191; J. Amer. Chem. Soc. 77:2919.
――――, W. A. ANDERSON, and J. T. ARNOLD, 1954. Nature 173:772.
―――― and T. C. LAURENT, 1954. J. Colloid Sci. 9:36.
JARDETZKY, C. D. and O. JARDETZKY, 1957. Biochim. Biophys. Acta 26:668.
―――― and ――――, 1962a. in Comprehensive Biochemistry, Vol. III (M. Florkin and E. H. Stotz, eds.), Elsevier, New York.
JARDETZKY, O., 1963. Personal communication.
―――― and R. J. BROWN, 1964. Personal communication.
―――― and C. D. JARDETZKY, 1962b. in Methods of Biochemical Analysis, Vol. IX (D. Glick, ed.), Interscience Publishers, New York.
JEFFREY, G. A., 1962. Dechema-Monographien 47:849.
―――― and R. K. MCMULLAN, 1962. J. Chem. Phys. 37:2231.
JOHNSON, G. A. and S. M. NEALE, 1961. J. Polymer Sci. 54:241.
JOSHI, S. K., 1961. J. Chem. Phys. 35:1141.

KAMB, W. B., 1963. Personal communication.
――――, 1964. Acta Cryst. (in press.)
―――― and S. K. DATTA, 1960. Nature 187:140; Acta Cryst. 13:1029.
KAMINSKY, M., 1957. Disc. Faraday Soc. 24:171; Z. Naturforsch. 12a:424.

KAVANAU, J. L., 1964. Structure and Function in Biological Membranes, Vols. I and II, Holden-Day, Inc., San Francisco.

KEAT, P. P., 1954. Science 120:338.

KENDREW, J. C., 1962. Brookhaven Symp. Biol. 15:216; in Enzyme Models and Enzyme Structure, p. 227, Office of Technical Services, U. S. Dept. of Commerce, Washington, D. C.

———, 1963. Science 139:1259.

KESSLER, YU. M., YU. M. POVAROV, and A. I. GORBANEV, 1962. J. Structural Chem. 3:82.

KING, E. L., 1959. J. Phys. Chem. 63:1070.

KIRKWOOD, J. G., 1939. J. Chem. Phys. 7:911.

———, 1957. in Molecular Structure and Biological Specificity, (L. Pauling and H. A. Itano, eds.), Waverly Press, Inc., Baltimore.

——— and J. B. SHUMAKER, 1952. Proc. Nat. Acad. Sci. 38:863.

KIRSHENBAUM, I., 1951. Physical Properties and Analysis of Heavy Water. National Nuclear Energy Series, Manhattan Project Technical Section, Division III, Vol. IVa, McGraw-Hill, New York.

KLOTZ, I. M., 1962. in Horizons in Biochemistry (M. Kasha and B. Pullman, eds.), Academic Press, New York.

KOEFOED, J., 1957. Disc. Faraday Soc. 24:216.

KÖNIG, H., 1942. Nachr. Akad. Wiss. Göttingen, No. 1, 1.

———, 1944. Z. Krist. 105:279.

KÖRÖSY, F., 1937. Trans. Faraday Soc. 33:416.

KRESGE, A. J., 1963. J. Chem. Phys. 39:1360.

KRESTOV, G. A., 1962. J. Structural Chem. 3:125.

KUJUMZELIS, TH. G., 1938. Z. Physik. 110:742.

LAIDLER, K. J., 1959. Canad. J. Chem. 37:138.

——— and C. PEGIS, 1957. Proc. Roy. Soc. A241:80.

LARSSON, K. E. and U. DAHLBORG, 1963. Internat. Atomic Energy Agency, Vienna.

———, S. HOLMRYD, and K. OTNES, 1960. Proc. Symp. on Inelastic Scattering of Neutrons in Solids and Liquids, Internat. Atomic Energy Agency, Vienna.

LATIMER, W. M., 1949. Chem. Rev. 44:59.

———, K. S. PITZER, and C. M. SLANSKY, 1939. J. Chem. Phys. 7:108.

LAURENT, T. C., 1957. Arkiv. Kemi 11:503.

LAVERGNE, M. and W. DROST-HANSEN, 1956. Naturwiss. 43:511.

LENNARD-JONES, J. and J. A. POPLE, 1951. Proc. Roy. Soc. A295:155.

LIDDEL, V. and N. F. RAMSEY, 1951. J. Chem. Phys. 19:1608.

LINDERSTRØM-LANG, K. U. and C. F. JACOBSEN, 1941. Compt. Rend. Trav. Lab. Carlsberg Ser. Chim. 24:1.

——— and J. A. SCHELLMAN, 1959. in The Enzymes (P. Boyer, H. Lardy and K. Myrback, eds.), Academic Press, New York.

LING, G. N., 1952. in Phosphorus Metabolism (W. O. McElroy and B. Glass, eds.), Johns Hopkins Press, Baltimore.

LIPPINCOTT, E. R., C. E. WEIR, and A. VAN VALKENBURG, 1960. J. Chem. Phys. 32:612.

LISGARTEN, N. D. and M. BLACKMAN, 1956. Nature 178:39.

LONDON, F., 1937. Trans. Faraday Soc. 33:8.

LONSDALE, D. K., 1958. Proc. Roy. Soc. **A247**:424.

LÖWDIN, P.-O., 1963. Rev. Modern Phys. **35**: 724.

LUZ, Z. and S. MEIBOOM, 1963a J. Chem. Phys. (in press.)

────── and ──────, 1963b. Personal communication.

MACY, H. H., 1952. Thesis, Univ. of London.

MAGNUSSON, L. B., 1963. J. Chem. Phys. **39**:1953.

──────, 1964. Personal communication.

MALENKOV, G. G., 1961. Doklady Akad. Nauk. S. S. S. R. **137**:1354.

──────, 1962. J. Structural Chem. **3**:206.

MASTERTON, W. L., 1954. J. Chem. Phys. **22**:1830.

MATYASH, I. V., M. A. PIONTOVSKAYA, and L. M. TARASENKO, 1962. J. Structural Chem. **3**:199.

MAYS, J. M. and G. W. BRADY, 1956. J. Chem. Phys. **25**:583.

McBAIN, J. W. and G. P. DAVIES, 1927. J. Amer. Chem. Soc. **49**:2230.

McFARLAN, R. L., 1936. Rev. Sci. Instr. **7**:82; J. Chem. Phys. **4**:60, 253.

McKOY, V. and O. SINANOGLU, 1963. J. Chem. Phys. **38**:2946.

McMULLAN, R. K., M. BONAMICO, and G. A. JEFFREY, 1963. J. Chem. Phys. **39**:3295.

MEGAW, H. D., 1934. Nature **134**:900.

MEIBOOM, S., 1961. J. Chem. Phys. **34**:375.

──────, Z. LUZ, and D. GILL, 1957. J. Chem. Phys. **28**:1611.

MIKHAILOV, I. G. and YU. P. SYRNIKOV, 1960. J. Structural Chem. **1**:10.

MILLER, A. A., 1963. J. Chem. Phys. **38**:1568.

MILLER, D. G., 1958. J. Amer. Chem. Soc. **80**:3576.

MISHCHENKO, K. P. and N. P. DYMARCHUK, 1962. J. Structural Chem. **3**:399.

MOELWYN-HUGHES, R. H., 1948. Proc. Cambridge Philos. Soc. **45**:477.

MORGAN, J. and B. E. WARREN, 1938. J. Chem. Phys. **6**:666.

MUKERJEE, P. 1961. J. Phys. Chem. **65**:740, 744.

NAMIOT, A. YU., 1961. J. Structural Chem. **2**:381, 444.

NÉMETHY, G. and H. A. SCHERAGA, 1962a. J. Chem. Phys. **36**:3382, 3401.

────── and ──────, 1962b. J. Phys. Chem. **66**:1773.

────── and ──────, 1964. Personal communication.

──────, I. Z. STEINBERG, and H. A. SCHERAGA, 1963. Biopolymers **1**:43.

NOYES, R. M., 1962. J. Amer. Chem. Soc. **84**:513.

ODAJIMA, A., J. SOHMA, and S. WATANABE, 1959. J. Chem. Phys. **31**:276.

ODEBLAD, E., 1959. Ann. New York Acad. Sci. **83**:189.

O'KONSKI, C. T., 1960. J. Phys. Chem. **64**:605.

──────, 1963. Rev. Modern Phys. **35**:732.

──────, 1964. Electrochemical Soc. Meeting, Symp. on Electrolytic Solutions, Toronto, Canada.

────── and A. J. HALTNER, 1957. J. Amer. Chem. Soc. **79**:5634.

────── and B. H. ZIMM, 1950. Science **111**:113.

ONSAGER, L., 1926. Physik. Z. **27**:388.

──────, 1927. Physik. Z. **28**:277.

──────, 1936. J. Amer. Chem. Soc. **58**:1486.

──────, 1945. Ann. New York Acad. Sci. **46**:241.

OPPENHEIMER, C. H. and W. DROST-HANSEN, 1959. J. Bacteriol. **80**:21.

OSTER, G. and J. G. KIRKWOOD, 1943. J. Chem. Phys. 11:175.
OSTWALD, W., 1928. Kolloid-Z. 46:248.
OWSTON, P. G., 1958. Adv. Phys. 7:171.

PADOVA, J., 1963. J. Chem. Phys. 39:1552.
———, 1964. J. Chem. Phys. 40:691.
PAKE, G. E., 1948. J. Chem. Phys. 16:327.
PAULING, L., 1935. J. Amer. Chem. Soc. 57:2680.
———, 1959. in Hydrogen Bonding. (D. Hadzi and H. W. Thompson, eds.), Pergamon Press, London.
———, 1960. The Nature of the Chemical Bond (3rd ed.), Cornell University Press, New York.
———, 1961. Science 134:15.
——— and R. E. MARSH, 1952. Proc. Nat. Acad. Sci. 38:112.
PEARSON, R. G., J. PALMER, M. M. ANDERSON, and A. L. ALLRED, 1960. Z. Elektrochem. 64:110.
PETERSON, S. W. and H. A. LEVY, 1957. Acta Cryst. 10:70.
PICKETT, A. G. and M. M. LEMCOE, 1959. J. Geophys. Res. 64:1579.
PIMENTEL, G. C. and A. L. McCLELLAN, 1960. The Hydrogen Bond, W. H. Freeman and Co., San Francisco.
POPLE, J. A., 1951. Proc. Roy. Soc. A205:163.
———, 1959. in Hydrogen Bonding (D. Hadzi and H. W. Thompson, eds.), Pergamon Press, London.
———, W. G. SCHNEIDER, and H. J. BERNSTEIN, 1959. High-Resolution Nuclear Magnetic Resonance, McGraw-Hill, New York.
POWELL, R. E. and W. M. LATIMER, 1951. J. Chem. Phys. 19:1139.
PRESSMAN, D., A. L. GROSSBERG, L. H. PENCE, and L. PAULING, 1946. J. Amer. Chem. Soc. 68:250.

RICHARDS, R. E. and J. A. SMITH, 1951. Trans. Faraday Soc. 47:1261.
RIL, N. V., 1955. Zhur. Fiz. Khim. 29:959, 1152, 1372, 1537.
RITSON, D. M. and J. B. HASTED, 1948. J. Chem. Phys. 16:11.
ROBERTS, J. D., 1961. An Introduction to the Analysis of Spin-Spin Splitting in High-Resolution Nuclear Magnetic Resonance Spectra, W. A. Benjamin, Inc., New York.
ROBINSON, R. A. and H. S. HARNED, 1941. Chem. Rev. 28:419.
——— and R. H. STOKES, 1959. Electrolyte Solutions, Butterworths, London.
RÖNTGEN, W. K., 1892. Ann. Phys. Chim. (Wied.) 45:91.
ROSSINI, F. D., 1952. Selected Values of Chemical Thermodynamic Properties, National Bureau of Standards, Washington, D. C.
———, D. D. WAGMAN, W. H. EVANS, S. LEVINE, and I. JAFFE, 1952. Nat. Bur. Stds. Circ. No. 500.
ROWLINSON, J. S., 1959. Liquids and Liquid Mixtures, Butterworths, London.

SAMOILOV, O. YA., 1946. Zhur. Fiz. Khim. 20:12.
———, 1955. Zhur. Fiz. Khim. 29:1582.
———, 1957a. Disc. Faraday Soc. 24:141, 216.

———, 1957b. Structure of Aqueous Electrolyte Solutions and Ion Hydration, Izd. Akad. Nauk. S. S. S. R., Moscow; also Die Struktur von Wassrigen Elektrolytlösungen, B. G. Teubner, Leipzig, 1961.

———, 1962. J. Structural Chem. 3:314.

SCHELLMAN, J. A., 1951. Thesis, Princeton Univ.

———, 1957. J. Chem. Phys. 26:1225.

——— and W. KAUTZMANN, 1951. Phys. Rev. 82:315.

SCHERAGA, H. A., 1960. Ann. New York Acad. Sci. 84:608.

SCHNEIDER, W. G., 1959. in Hydrogen Bonding (D. Hadzi and H. W. Thompson, eds.), Pergamon Press, London.

SCHWARZENBACH, G., 1936. Z. Physik. Chem. B176:133.

SEARS, R. E., 1960. New Zealand J. Sci. 3:127.

SHALLCROSS, F. V. and G. B. CARPENTER, 1957. J. Chem. Phys. 26:782.

SHOOLERY, J. N. and B. J. ALDER, 1955. J. Chem. Phys. 23:805.

SIMONS, L., 1939. Soc. Sci. Fennica, Commentationes Phys. Math. 10, No. 9.

SINANOGLU, O., V. McKOY, and S. ABDULNUR, 1963. Abstr., Meeting Amer. Chem. Soc., New York.

SINGWI, K. S. and A. SJÖLANDER, 1960. Phys. Rev. 119:863.

SOKOLOV, N. D., 1956. Tagesbericht der Chem. Gesell. in der Deutschen Demokratischen Republik, Hauptjarestagung 1955, Akademie-Verlag, Berlin.

SPONSLER, O. L., J. D. BATH, and J. W. ELLIS, 1940. J. Phys. Chem. 35:2053.

SQUIRE, P., P. MOSER, and C. T. O'KONSKI, 1964. Studies in progress.

STACKELBERG, M. VON, 1949. Naturwiss. 36:327, 359.

——— and H. R. MÜLLER, 1954. Z. Elektrochem. 58:25.

——— and W. JAHNS, 1954. Z. Elektrochem. 58:162.

STECKEL, F. and S. SZAPIRO, 1963. Trans. Faraday Soc. 59:331.

STELLWAGEN, N. C., M. SHIRAI, and C. T. O'KONSKI, 1964. Biophys. J. Submitted for publication.

STEWART, G. W., 1934. J. Chem. Phys. 2:558.

———, 1939. J. Chem. Phys. 7:869.

———, 1943. J. Chem. Phys. 11:72.

———, 1944. J. Chem. Phys. 12:321.

STOKES, R. H. and R. A. ROBINSON, 1948. J. Amer. Chem. Soc. 70:1870.

SUHRMANN, R. and F. BREYER, 1933. Z. Physik. Chem. B20:17; B23:193.

——— and I. WIEDERSICH, 1953. Z. Anorg. Chem. 272:167; Z. Elektrochem. 57:93.

SUTRA, G., 1946. J. Chim. Phys. 43:189, 319.

SWAIN, C. G. and R. F. BADER, 1960. Tetrahedron 10:182.

SWIFT, T. J. and R. E. CONNICK, 1962. J. Chem. Phys. 37:307.

SYRNIKOV, YU. P., 1958. Doklady Akad. Nauk. S. S. S. R. 118:760.

TAMMANN, G., 1900. Ann. Phys. 2:1.

TANFORD, C., 1962. in Discussion, Enzyme Models and Enzyme Structure, p. 227, Office of Technical Services, U.S. Dept. of Commerce, Washington, D. C.

TURKEVICH, J., J. MACKAY, and W. H. THOMAS, 1960. Actes Congress Internat. Catalyse, 2e, Paris.

UHLIG, H. H., 1937. J. Phys. Chem. 41:1215.

ULICH, H., 1936. Z. Angew. Chem. 49:279.

VASLOW, F., 1963. J. Phys. Chem. **67**:2773.

VEGARD, L. and S. HILLESUND, 1942. Avh. Norske Vidensk. Akad., No. **8**, 1.

VERWEY, E. J., 1942. Rec. Trav. Chim. **61**:564.

VOLLMER, P. M., 1963. J. Chem. Phys. **39**:2236.

WAALS, J. H. VAN DER and J. C. PLATTEEUV, 1958. Mol. Phys. **1**:91.

WADA, G., 1961. Bull. Chem. Soc. Japan **34**:955.

WAGNER, K. W., 1915. Elektrotechn. Z. **36**:111, 121, 135, 163.

WALDRON, R. D., 1957. J. Chem. Phys. **26**:809.

WANG, J. H., 1951. J. Amer. Chem. Soc. **73**:4181.

——, 1954a. J. Amer. Chem. Soc. **76**:4755.

——, 1954b. J. Phys. Chem. **58**:686.

——, 1955. J. Chem. Phys. **77**:258.

WERTZ, J. E., 1955. Chem. Rev. **55**:829.

WHALLEY, E., 1963. J. Chem. Phys. **38**:1400.

WHITE, J. L. and A. F. BURNS, 1963. Science **141**:800.

WICKE, E., M. EIGEN, and TH. ACKERMANN, 1954. Z. Physik. Chem. **1**:340.

WILLIAMS, D. and T. N. GAUTIER, 1939. Phys. Rev. **56**:616.

—— and W. MILLET, 1944. Phys. Rev. **66**:6.

WILLIAMS, R. B., 1958. Ann. New York Acad. Sci. **70**:763.

WINSOR, P. A., 1954. Solvent Properties of Amphiphilic Compounds, Butterworths, London.

WIRTZ, K., 1947. Angew. Chem. **A59**:138.

WOLLAN, E. O., W. L. DAVIDSON, and C. G. SHULL, 1949. Phys. Rev. **75**:1348.

WYATT, P. A., 1957. Disc. Faraday Soc. **24**:162.

WYMAN, J., 1930. Phys. Rev. **35**:623.

YOON, Y. K. and G. B. CARPENTER, 1959. Acta Cryst. **12**:17.

ZACHARIASEN, W. H., 1954. *in* The Actinide Elements, Vol. 14A (G. T. Seaborg and J. J. Katz, eds.), McGraw-Hill, New York.

AUTHOR INDEX

Kamb, W. B., 3, 4, 83
Kaminsky, M., 59, 60, 83
Karassev, V. V., 34, 80
Kasha, M., 84
Katz, J. J., 88
Kautzmann, W., 5, 87
Kavanau, J. L., 27, 77, 78, 83
Keat, P. P., 4, 83
Kendrew, J. C., 32, 44, 83
Kessler, Yu. M., 55, 84
King, E. L., 70, 84
Kirkwood, J. G., 20, 30, 31, 34, 56, 75, 84, 85
Kirschner, S., 81
Kirshenbaum, I., 21, 84
Kitamura, N., 2, 83
Kleinzeller, A., 81
Kley, W., 18, 83
Klotz, I. M., 23, 47, 52, 84
Koefoed, J., 12, 84
König, H., 2, 3, 84
Körösy, F., 22, 84
Kotzk, A., 81
Krause, J. T., 8, 64, 80
Kresge, A. J., 64, 84
Krestov, G. A., 60, 84
Krogh-Moe, J., 20, 82
Kujumzelis, Th. G., 44, 65, 84

Laidler, K. J., 57, 64, 70, 80, 84
Lardy, H., 84
Larsson, K. E., 18, 84
Larsson, S., 18, 84
Latimer, W. M., 5, 24, 53, 54, 57, 70, 84, 86
Laurent, T. C., 36, 37, 83, 84
Lavergne, M., 13, 84
Lemcoe, M. M., 43, 86
Lennard-Jones, J., 62, 84
Lester, G., 41–43, 45, 83
Levine, S., 67, 86
Levy, H. A., 1, 8, 10, 18, 80, 86
Liddel, V., 39, 84
Linderstrøm-Lang, K. U., 30, 84
Ling, G. N., 52, 84
Linton, H., 48, 80
Lippincott, E. R., 3, 84
Lisgarten, N. D., 2, 79, 84
London, F., 25, 84
Lonsdale, D. K., 2, 84
Löwdin, P.-O., 50, 84
Lubas, B., 42, 80
Luz, Z., 50, 51, 75–77, 84, 85

Macy, H. H., 34, 85
Mackay, J., 43, 87
Magnusson, L. B., 66, 68, 70–72, 85
Malenkov, G. G., 14, 20, 23, 85
Marsh, R. E., 14, 86
Masterton, W. L., 26, 27, 85
Matyash, I. V., 43, 85

Mays, J. M., 36, 85
McBain, J. W., 34, 85
McClellan, A. L., 20, 21, 39, 70, 86
McElroy, W. O., 84
McFarlan, R. L., 3, 85
McKoy, V., 15, 23, 85, 87
McLaren, A. D., 28, 81
McMullan, R. K., 15, 24, 55, 79, 83, 85
McNiven, N., 41–43, 45, 83
Megaw, H. D., 20, 85
Meiboom, S., 39, 40, 50, 51, 75–77, 84, 85
Mendel, H., 20, 81
Mihama, K., 2, 83
Mikhailov, I. G., 8, 20, 58, 61, 85
Miller, A. A., 13, 85
Miller, D. G., 59, 85
Millet, W., 65, 88
Mishchenko, K. P., 65, 85
Moelwyn-Hughes, R. H., 55, 85
Morgan, J., 8, 85
Morrison, J. A., 3, 79
Moser, P., 47, 87
Mukerjee, P., 57, 64, 85
Müller, H. R., 14, 18, 87
Myrback, K., 84

Namiot, A. Yu., 20, 23, 24, 26, 85
Neale, S. M., 46, 83
Némethy, G., 11–14, 17, 19–22, 25, 26, 32, 76, 85
Neville, H. A., 34, 83
Nissan, H. A., 20, 82
Noyes, R. M., 30, 31, 54, 55, 57, 70, 85

Odajima, A., 41, 42, 85
Odeblad, E., 41, 85
O'Konski, C. T., 5, 45–47, 53, 55, 60, 70, 71, 82, 85, 87
Oliver, W. F., 2, 80
Oncley, J. L., 46, 81
Onsager, L., 30, 45, 73, 82, 85
Oppenheimer, C. H., 13, 85
Oster, G., 20, 85
Ostwald, W., 34, 85
Otnes, K., 18, 84
Overbeek, J. Th., 46, 81
Owston, P. G., 1, 85

Packard, M. E., 39, 79
Padova, J., 30, 31, 57, 61, 62, 64, 86
Pake, G. E., 39, 86
Palevsky, H., 18, 83
Palmer, J., 75, 86
Pare, X., 43, 79
Pauling, L., 1, 14–17, 19, 30, 32, 81, 86
Pearson, R. G., 75, 86
Pegis, C., 57, 64, 70, 84
Pence, L. H., 30, 86
Peterson, S. W., 1, 86

Pickett, A. G., 43, 86
Pimentel, G. C., 20, 21, 39, 70, 83, 86
Piontovskaya, M. A., 43, 85
Pitzer, K. S., 54, 57, 84
Platteeuv, J. C., 15, 88
Polglas, M. F., 23, 80
Pople, J. A., 19, 20, 32, 37, 39, 62, 81, 84, 86
Poulson, R. E., 75, 80
Povarov, Yu. M., 55, 84
Powell, R. E., 24, 53, 70, 86
Pressman, D., 30, 86
Pullman, B., 84

Quist, A. S., 17–19, 82

Ramsey, N. F., 39, 84
Reding, E. P., 3, 83
Redlich, O., 50, 83
Reilly, C. A., 50, 83
Richards, R. E., 30, 47, 86
Rideal, E. K., 28, 34, 52, 80
Ril, N. V., 36, 86
Rinfret, A. P., 2, 3, 81
Ritson, D. M., 11, 30, 55, 59, 73, 80, 82, 86
Roberts, J. D., 37, 86
Robertson, R. E., 23, 82
Robinson, A. L., 54, 59, 82
Robinson, J. D., 45, 83
Robinson, R. A., 8, 47, 55, 86, 87
Roderick, G. W., 73, 82
Romanow, W. J., 8, 80
Röntgen, W. K., 8, 13, 86
Rossini, F. D., 30, 67, 86
Rowlinson, J. S., 24, 86

Sack, H., 46, 81
Saika, A., 50, 82
Samoilov, O. Ya., 1, 10, 19, 28, 29, 32, 58, 60, 61, 86
Schellman, J. A., 5, 30, 84, 87
Scheraga, H. A., 11–14, 17, 19–22, 25, 26, 32, 76, 85, 87
Schneider, W. G., 37, 39, 86, 87
Schmitt, F. O., 82
Schwarz, G., 76, 81
Schwarzenbach, G., 30, 87
Seaborg, G. T., 88
Sears, R. E., 43, 87
Shallcross, F. V., 2, 87
Shimaoka, K., 2, 3, 83
Shirai, M., 46, 87
Shoolery, J. N., 28, 39, 57, 66, 74, 83, 87
Shull, C. G., 1, 88
Shumaker, J. B., 52, 75, 84
Simons, L., 8, 87
Sinanoglu, O., 15, 23, 85, 87
Singwi, K. S., 14, 18, 87
Sjölander, A., 14, 18, 87
Slanksy, C. M., 54, 57, 84

Smith, J. A., 30, 47, 86
Sohama, J., 41, 42, 85
Sokolov, N. D., 10, 87
Sponsler, O. L., 32, 87
Squire, P., 47, 87
Stackelberg, M. von, 14, 15, 18, 87
Steckel, F., 22, 87
Steinberg, I. Z., 32, 85
Stellwagen, N. C., 46, 87
Stewart, G. W., 22, 52, 87
Stokes, R. H., 8, 47, 55, 86, 87
Stotz, E. H., 83
Stover, E. D., 75, 80
Suhrmann, R., 58, 59, 65, 73, 75, 87
Sutra, G., 58, 60, 87
Swain, C. G., 21, 87
Swift, T. J., 29, 75, 87
Syrnikov, Yu. P., 8, 20, 55, 58, 61, 85, 87
Szapiro, S., 22, 87
Szczepkowski, T. W., 42, 80

Tammann, G., 2, 3, 87
Tanford, C., 32, 87
Tarasenko, L. M., 43, 85
Taube, H., 29, 83
Thomas, W. H., 43, 87
Thompson, H. W., 80, 86, 87
Titijevskaya, A. S., 34, 80
Tunkelo, E., 18, 83
Turkevich, J., 43, 87
Turnbull, D., 14, 80

Uhlig, H. H., 22, 87
Ulich, H., 58, 87

Valkenburg, A. van, 3, 84
Vaslow, F., 56, 72, 87
Vegard, L., 2, 87
Verwey, E. J., 28, 55, 88
Viervoll, H., 8, 82
Vinograd, J., 33, 44, 83
Vollmer, P. M., 54, 59, 88

Waals, J. H. van der, 15, 88
Wada, G., 20, 88
Wagner, K. W., 45, 88
Wagman, D. D., 67, 86
Waldron, R. D., 55, 88
Walker, G. F., 43, 82
Wang, J. H., 21, 36, 58, 59, 88
Warren, B. E., 8, 85
Watanabe, S., 41, 42, 85
Weir, C. E., 3, 84
Weissmann, M., 6, 80
Wen, W.-Y., 10–12, 17, 25, 28, 53, 59, 60, 62, 64, 65, 82
Wertz, J. E., 38, 88
West, G. W., 43, 82
Whalley, E., 3, 4, 57, 79, 88

SUBJECT INDEX

Intermediate structure-broken region, 53, 64, 65
Internal pressure
  n-hexane, 26
  water, 26
Intracrystalline water, 43
Intrinsic radius of ions in solution, 57, 62, 64
Ion-dipole interactions, 28
  coupling energy, 57, 60, 70
Ionic mobility (see Mobility)
Ion-ion interactions, 71, 72
Ionization
  potential, 67, 68
  process, 68
Ion-pairing, 55, 65, 66, 78
Ion-quadrupole interaction, 56
Ion-water interactions, 28–31, 52–78
  covalent approach to, 66, 72
Irrotational binding, 42, 55
Isotopic studies, 1, 3, 20–22, 29, 51, 75, 77

Keatite, 4
Kerr effect (see Birefringence, electrical)
Kirkwood theory, 20, 30, 56
Krypton hydrate, 15

Larmor precession frequencies, 38–40, 51
Lattice
  deformation, 7, 60, 63, 65
    geometrical (steric), 7, 60, 63
    relaxational, 7
      in bond angles, 7
      in bond lengths, 7
    vibrations, 60, 63
  distortion (see Lattice deformation)
  energy, 1
  glide (dislocation), 63
  order, 41
  points, quasi, 23
Lattice defects, 5–7, 9
  annihilation of, 9, 62
  diffusion of, 7, 9
  formation of, 5–7, 9, 53, 62
  in ice, 5–7
    jumping of, 7
  in water, 9, 10
Librational motion, 24
Lifetime broadening, 39
Lifetimes of coordinated water molecules, 29, 33
Ligands, 29
Lipid head groups, functions of, 77, 78
Localized hydrolysis, 55
London forces (see Transient-dipole induced dipole interactions)
Lone interstitial molecules (see Water molecules, lone interstitial)
Lone-pair electrons, 10, 12, 20, 55, 62

Long-range ordering
  of protons, 3
  of water, 34–47
Lorentzian line, 40, 51

Macromolecular solutions, 33–47
Magnetic field
  inhomogeneity, 38, 42
  intensity, 37, 38
Magnetic fields
  oscillating local, 40
  rotating, 37, 40
  stationary, 37, 41
Mass spectroscopy, 47
Maxwell-Wagner theory, 45
Melting point
  of deuterium oxide, 20
Melting process, 9
Membrane transformations, 52, 78
Methane, 26, 27
Methane hydrate, 15
Methanol, 75
Methylammonium ion, 76
Methyl and methylene groups, 24, 27, 76, 77
  functions of at membrane interfaces, 76, 77
Methylammonium ion, 76
Micellar interfaces, 36, 47
Mobility
  of counterions, 45, 51, 52
  of ions, 47–50, 52
  of protons, 40, 43, 47–52
Molal volume
  apparent, 58
  ionic, 52
Molar volumes, 13, 22, 26, 54
Molecular ions, 47, 59, 62, 63, 72
Montmorillonite, 43
Myoglobin, 44
Myosin solutions, 41

Nectorite, 43
Némethy-Scheraga model of water structure, 12–14, 21
Neutron
  diffraction, 1
  scattering, 18, 19
Nitrate ion solutions, 50
Nitrilotriacetate ion, 29
Noble-gas-type ions, 31, 53, 68, 71
Nontronite, 43
Nuclear magnetic moment, 37
Nuclear magnetic resonance, 24, 29, 33, 36–44, 50, 60–64, 72, 74–77
  area under signal, 38, 43
  frequency, 37
  high resolution, 37, 38, 43
  line broadening, 39–41, 43